Essential Principles of Signals Collection and Analysis

For a complete listing of titles in the
Artech House Intelligence and Information Operations Library,
please turn to the back of this book.

Essential Principles of Signals Collection and Analysis

David A. Garren
Uttam K. Majumder
Erik P. Blasch

ARTECH
HOUSE
BOSTON | LONDON
artechhouse.com

Library of Congress Cataloging-in-Publication Data
A catalog record for this book is available from the U.S. Library of Congress.

ISBN-13: 978-1-63081-643-8

Cover design by Mark Bergeron

685 Canton Street
Norwood, MA 02062

10 9 8 7 6 5 4 3 2 1

Contents

3

Access to RF Signals 33

4

Radar Fundamentals 49

Foreword

Since WWII, the discipline of signals intelligence (SIGINT) has undergone dramatic changes as communication technology has revolutionized in many dimensions. Increased frequencies greatly expanded bandwidths, along with complex digital and spectral encoding, and advanced encryption, to increase the capability of electronic communication and the difficulty of collecting signals intelligence. Not only have technology advances challenged signals collection; the ubiquity and scale of channels to intercept have demanded greater capacity and selectivity on the part of the intelligence collector. The targets of intercept include vehicles and vessels, satellites, handhelds and tracking tags, and pervasive mobile systems and computer networks. The scope of modern SIGINT is global and encompasses foreign military, government, and civilian channels that pose threats and become targets of collection.

SIGINT encompasses a wide range of signals applications that include, individually or in combination, communications intelligence (COMINT), electronic intelligence (ELINT), and foreign instrumentation signals intelligence (FISINT). The terms SIGINT, communications, or information often apply to all forms of communications, noncommunications, and data regulated by the appropriate intelligence legal definitions, closely allying SIGINT with cyber intelligence exploitation and computer surveillance. SIGINT is also related to the discipline of cryptology—the study and applications of signal encoding, encryption, and decryption.

Computing technology has enabled ever-expanding forms of processing information to characterize and understand signals and communication content. The role of SIGINT is to convert information into an intelligible form intended for human analysis, including decryption or cryptanalysis. Analytic activities include correlating, geolocating, and combining signals data with other sources (geospatial, GEOINT; human, HUMINT; measurement and signals, MASINT) to increase the value of the intelligence collected. Current processing enables bulk collection of communications, metadata analysis, contact chaining, and call network analysis at significant scales.

Of course, the specific sources and unique methods of SIGINT remain sensitive and cannot be shared openly. The U.S. National Security Agency (NSA) has declassified and published many historical and practical descriptions of the methods used, and this book provides a coherent and comprehensive introduction that has been prepublication reviewed and approved for publication.

This book provides a clear and comprehensive introduction to the discipline and methods of SIGINT by uniquely qualified experts in the field. It is an important addition to signals intelligence literature and an essential addition to the bookshelf of any intelligence officer, intelligence system developer, or manager.

Ed Waltz
Series Editor, Artech House
Intelligence and Information Operations Series
July 2023

1

Introduction to Signals Collection and Analysis

1.1 Key Foundations

This book is an introductory text describing the fundamentals of signals collection and processing. This material will equip the graduate student or engineering practitioner with the basic concepts and skills required to manage and develop systems for collecting and processing signals. Key foundations and principles describe the processes of collecting and analyzing signals from an uncooperative source, formulated from physical and signal theoretic concepts. As a technical text, it applies the foundational principles and concepts to the collection and exploitation of uncooperative signals of interest. Finally, it provides references for further study of signals intelligence analysis.

The topic of *signals collection* is fundamentally equivalent to that of a noncooperative communications system. In a traditional cooperative communications system, the transmitter and the receiver are designed to optimally send the required information over a particular channel. Both the transmitter and receiver systems agree upon the basic external signal parameters, such as center frequency, bandwidth, and modulation type, prior to the transmission of any actual signals. In addition, both the transmitter and receiver agree upon the standards used for the signal internals, including multiplexing, encoding, forward error correction, encryption, and other processing steps that are applied to a data stream. Furthermore, the signals' internal data stream can include the overall details of the protocol stack, which is used along with the Transmission Control Protocol/Internet Protocol (TCP/IP). It is assumed with cooperation communication that a moderate-to-high level of security is applied in maintaining the fidelity, confidentiality, availability, and integrity of the data that is transmitted cooperatively over the intended channel.

Entering one or more noncooperative signal receivers into the environment requires signals analysis or signals intelligence (SIGINT). Generally, the primary purpose of any *noncooperative receiver* is to intercept the intended communication without alerting the cooperative communications system of these surveillance activities. The scenario involves two actors, blue and red, to denote self and adversary. Throughout the text, the words red-force and adversary are used to denote the overall system from players of an opposing cooperative communications system. It is presumed that nefarious clandestine messages are being sent from the transmitter to the intended receiver. Thus, the noncooperative blue force receiver attempts to intercept, demodulate, demultiplex, decode, and extract the intended message stream for further analysis.

The text also discusses *spoofing*, wherein the noncooperative system acts not only as a receiver, but also as a transmitter. In such cases, the noncooperative system analyzes the intercepted signal so that strategic decisions can be made pertaining to the desired modifications of the signals in order to affect blue-force outcomes. Specifically, the blue force transmits the fabricated modified signals so that it will be intercepted by the originally intended receiver and processed by the system accordingly. The goal is for the adversary receiver to process the fabricated blue-force signal instead of the original signal sent by the red-force transmitter. As a result, the red force conducts actions which are favorable to the blue force after receiving the spoofed signals.

For the applications considered in the text, the communications channel is from the transmission of electromagnetic (EM) radiation from one location to another. For most applications, the analysis concentrates on bands of radiation that are associated with conventional microwave radiation. The bands include the high-frequency (HF) bands of MHz up to the K, Ka, and Ku bands in the 10 to 40

GHz span. Lower frequencies can be used, but often the required antenna sizes are quite large and the associated data rates are relatively low. However, the physical size of the corresponding energy distribution from the antenna is very broad spatially, which eases the requirements of signal intercept. At the high end of the radio spectrum, small antenna sizes with extremely high transmission data rates are possible. However, the beamwidth of the main energy beam is quite narrow, which increases the difficulty of performing successful signal intercept. At the even higher frequency bands of infrared (IR) and electro-optical (EO), the beamwidth of a laser link can be the size of the receiving platform. For such cases, signal intercept becomes even more difficult.

There are several issues that determine the ability to successfully intercept a red-force signal. At the most fundamental level, the blue-force intercept receiver must receive sufficient signal strength above the background noise and interference to be able to detect the signal and extract its basic external parameters. Signal processing often includes the ability to demodulate the received signal into its intended stream of digital symbols. The ability to perform noncooperative intercept depends primarily on the properties of the receiver antenna and the location and orientation of this antenna relative to that of the transmitting red-force antenna. Specifically, the red-force transmitter can have properties of spatial, temporal, and polarization diversity for sending the desired signal waveforms. Likewise, the blue-force antenna system can have these same properties available to best receive the red-force signal. In addition, signal intercept can occur in either the mainbeam, or one of the sidelobes of the transmission antenna beam pattern. Overall, it is the interplay of the red-force transmitter diversity and the blue-force receiver diversity that determine the possible signal-to-noise plus interference (SINR) which is available for processing within the noncooperative receiver system. This text includes examples of the requirements to successfully extract a desired received signal.

If the blue-force receiver can detect a noncooperative signal above the energy level of the competing interference and noise, then it is often possible to estimate the location of the transmitter. Various techniques can be applied, which depend upon the number of blue-force receivers that are able to intercept the red-force signal. If only a single blue-force receiver can detect the signal above the background noise and cochannel interference, then basic interferometric techniques must be used. These methods are often called *angle of arrival (AoA)* techniques and rely upon the use of multiple receiver phase elements to estimate the direction a signal is arriving at the blue-force receiver. Note that noncooperative signal intercept does not directly convey the range to the red-force transmitter, unless the transmitted signal itself contains information regarding the actual transmission time; and, if such information can be deemed reliable, and not a deliberate attempt to mislead any noncooperative receivers in the vicinity. However, the range to the transmitter can be inferred in many cases, especially if there is prior knowledge or hypotheses that the transmitter lies on the surface of the Earth. In such situations, the uncertainty AoA mainbeam can be intersected with the surface of the Earth to determine the region in which the transmitter is likely to lie.

If the signal is received by two or more intercept receivers, then additional techniques can be applied. Suppose that a given signal is received by two receivers lying at different physical locations. Ideally, assume that the noise and interference are relatively weak, so that both blue-force antennas receive approximately the same signal. In general, one of the two blue-force receivers is closer to the red-force transmitter than the other. Thus, the nearer antenna will receive this signal at an earlier time than that for the other antenna, due to the approximate constancy of the speed of light in the Earth's atmosphere and the space environment. The determination of this time difference can be obtained by correlating the signal received by one antenna with various time-delayed versions of this same signal received by another antenna. In this context, the term time delay includes negative values wherein the signal is received at the second antenna before it is received at the first antenna. This estimated *time difference of arrival (TDOA)* can be translated into a range difference to the transmitter, based upon the approximate constancy of the speed of light in these domains. The TDOA estimate limits the locus of possible locations for the red-force transmitter. If the transmitter is assumed to lie on the surface of the Earth, then the locus of possible transmitter locations is restricted further. This analysis presents specific examples of determining the location of a transmitter based upon these techniques.

Radar waveforms exhibit another useful property in determining transmitter location due to the Doppler effect. If there is a nonzero relative velocity along the line of sight from a given transmitter to a receiver, then the frequency of the received waveform will be shifted relative to that which was transmitted. Thus, if two different noncooperative antennas receive a given signal, then this received signal will lie, in general, at different center frequencies. Also note that the blue-force system will not know the actual center frequency of the transmitted signal unless this waveform contains embedded information regarding the center frequency, and if such information can be trusted. However, although the true transmitted frequency is not known to the blue-force, the antennas will measure relative frequency shift between the two signals. Estimates for this *frequency difference of arrival (FDOA)* can be obtained by using appropriate correlation techniques involving the two received signal streams. This FDOA estimate is also able to limit the locus of possible transmitter locations, which can be further restricted if the transmitter is assumed to lie on the surface of the Earth. In addition, these TDOA and FDOA methods can be combined to better provide an accurate estimate of the target location. The use of estimates based upon multiple pairs of blue-force receivers can enhance the accuracy of the transmitter location further.

Even after the blue-force receiver detects the noncooperative signal lying at a center frequency and bandwidth, there remain the challenges of demodulation. If the blue-force receiver has prior knowledge of the red-force modulation scheme, then the appropriate *demodulation techniques* can be applied—just as if this communication intercept were of the cooperative variety. However, in general, the blue-force receiver does not possess prior knowledge of the demodulation scheme so that it is necessary to apply specific techniques to determine which method of signal modulation is being used. For example, the red-force transmitter can use amplitude modulation (AM), frequency modulation (FM), binary phase shift keying (BPSK), quadrature phase shift keying (QPSK), N-PSK (N-symbol phase shift keying), quadrature amplitude modulation (QAM), and a combination of these basic schemes. After determination of the specific type of modulation, the blue-force receiver system can demodulate the signal to generate the received symbols that can be translated into a digital bitstream. For cases of lower SINR, there is a greater probability of demodulation errors that result in corresponding errors in the received bit pattern.

The demodulation of the received red-force signal to yield the internals of the bitstream presents additional challenges. It is necessary to determine any existing multiplexing schemes to extract the various information streams. Then, it may be necessary to determine the encryption codes in order to extract an accurate version of the signal copy of the actual text, fax, audio, or video of a given information stream.

After the demodulation of the signal symbols into a bitstream, additional analysis is often required to decipher this signal internals information. In many cases, the critical information of interest has been encrypted according to various possible schemes. One methodology is based upon single-key *cryptography*, as shown in Figure 1.1. In this technique there is a single shared symmetric key K, which enables the encryption $E\{\cdot\}$ of the message M to yield the corresponding ciphertext C. This ciphertext C is sent to the receiving station and appears to be an unintelligible random bit sequence to any unintended recipient who does not possess the key K that is shared between the intended users. At the receiving station, this ciphertext C is entered into an decryption algorithm $D\{\cdot\}$ that effectively undoes all of the permutations and mixing of the encryption algorithm $E\{\cdot\}$ by using the same shared key K in order to yield the original message M.

1.2 Presentation Organization

The remainder of this book details the various steps involved in signals collection and processing from a technical perspective. The focus is on the mathematical fundamentals rather than on generating specific optimal solutions. However, the goal of this text is to provide the reader with the fundamental concepts and mathematical

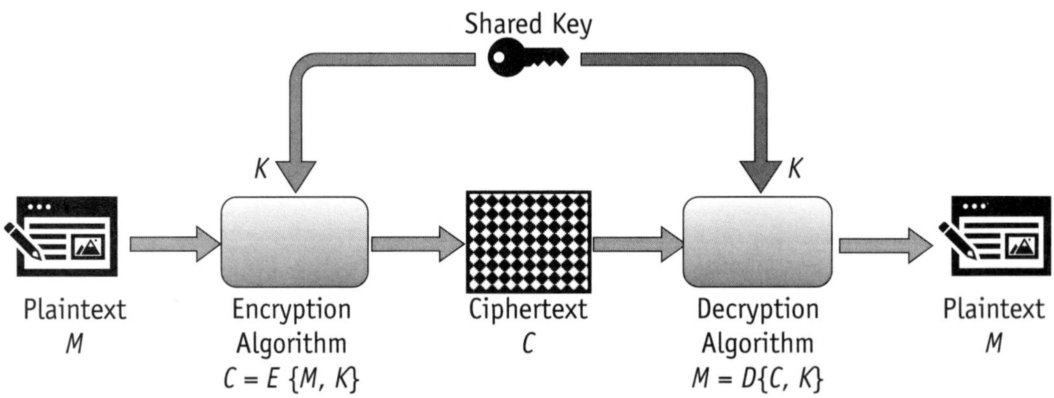

Figure 1.1
Model of single-key symmetric cryptography.

techniques to generate desired systems based upon a specific set of requirements.

In Chapter 2, we provide a summary of the fundamentals for the processing of emitter and communications signals required for the remainder of the book. Chapter 3 describes the core concepts and essential parameters needed for accessing signals from spaceborne platforms. Chapter 4 develops the core concepts to propagate the radio waveforms from a transmitting antenna, through an intervening medium, to the receiver antenna. This chapter includes discussions of radar beamwidth and the radar-range equation.

Chapter 5 describes the TDOA and FDOA processing needed to estimate the locations of uncooperative emitters, including radar and communications terminals. Chapter 6 explains the mathematical concepts for detecting signals and the estimation of signals externals, such as center frequency, bandwidth, modulation type, and others. Chapter 7 provides a summary of the cryptographic techniques that are used to protect communications bitstreams.

Chapter 8 explores basic concepts for the transmission of signals within the networks of the internet. In Chapter 9, machine learning (ML) and deep-learning neural networks (DNN) (e.g., see Figure 1.2) are explored for application to the exploitation of signals, including automatic target classification. Future trends for signals collection and exploitation are examined in Chapter 10.

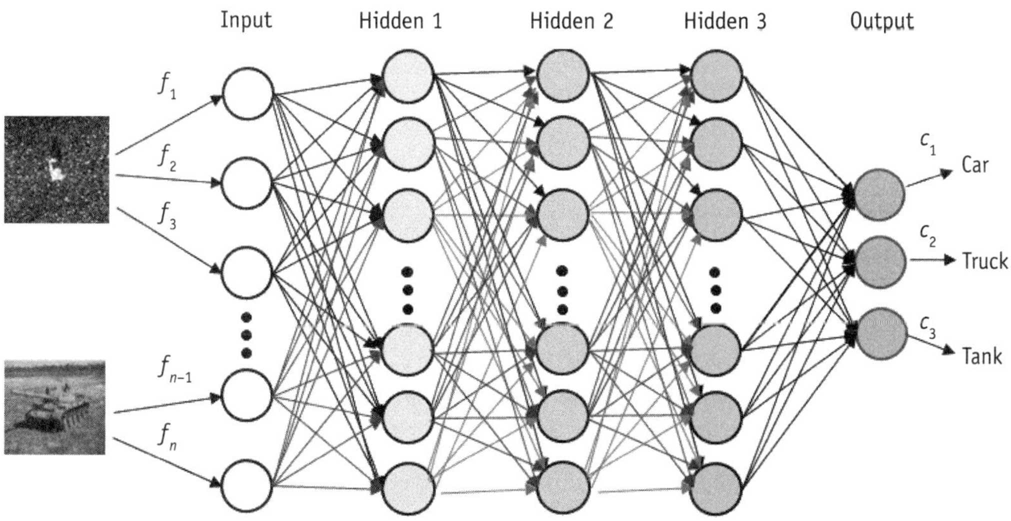

Figure 1.2
Deep-learning neural network for automatic target classification.

2

RF Signals Classification

2.1 Introduction

Radio frequency (RF) communication systems are present in many aspects of our daily life. For example, mobile telecommunication systems (smartphones) are built upon wireless RF communications. In the home, the radio and television are connected to a wireless access point (WAP) via RF signals such as Wi-Fi 802.11. In fact, modern homes are built on the concept of IoT (Internet of Things) devices wherein all the electronics (home security systems, smartphones, smart watches, radio, television, remote car starters, personal assistants) can be connected to Wi-Fi and Bluetooth devices. *Cognition* is the ability to gain understanding through sensing, which enables context awareness. Hence, the connected devices introduce the concept of cognitive RF systems, where RF systems can sense the environments autonomously and help users effortlessly make decisions. In an *industrial setting*, a cognitive RF system can be thought of as a network of RF identification (RFID) transponders (both transmitter and receiver). In a *surveillance system*, multiband cognitive radar can adapt due to environmental changes. Finally, cognitive communications are evident with software-defined radios (SDR), networks (SDN), and infrastructure (SDI).

Machine learning (ML) algorithms evolved from classifying images of speech, behaviors, and text [1–4] as well as providing recommendations among different choices. ML applications are evident in medical diagnoses, financial markets, IoT [5], and cyber security [6]. Also, in a *multidomain scenario* of information from satellites and broadcast signals, cognition through machine learning builds patterns of tracks and behaviors [7]. Most recently, ML has been considered for classifying radio RF communication signals and self-driving cars. The focus of this chapter is how ML can be used to classify RF communication signals. ML can be used for developing a cognitive RF system [8, 9] such as enhancements in software signal processing, analysis of received signals analysis, and hardware emitter classification.

A RF cognitive system can sense the environment and adjust parameters (frequency, bandwidth, and code) based on the functionality. Cognitive RF approaches utilize machine-learning methods. Invoking the popular observe, orient, decide, act (OODA) loop, a cognitive radios/RF approach also creates plans by learning from the collections (Figure 2.1). For example, a cognitive RF system can use *antenna beamforming* to send signals to a particular spatial area to avoid interference or improve transmission. In fact,

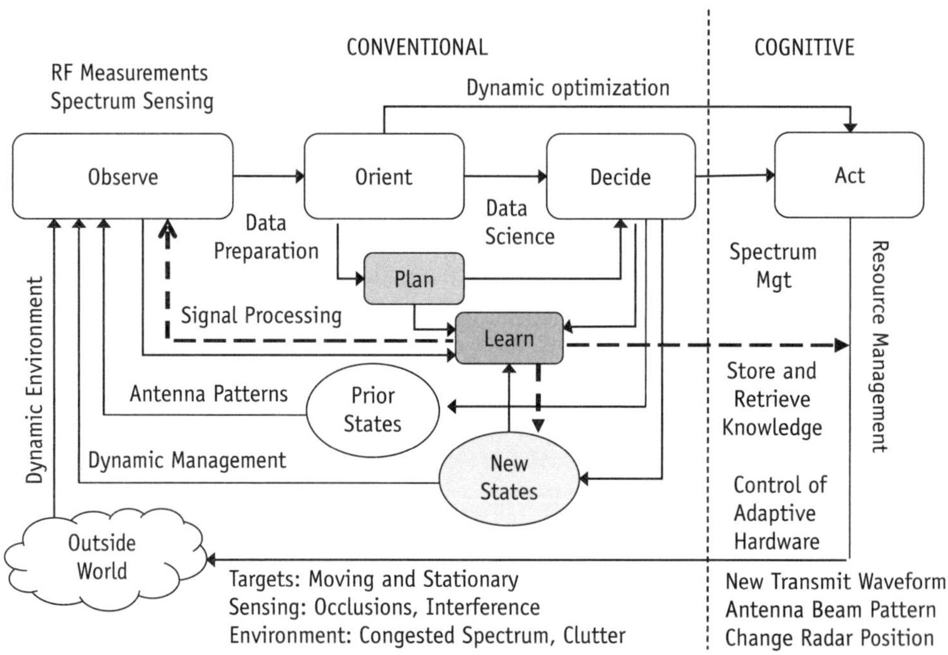

Figure 2.1
Cognitive RF design.

the IEEE Wi-Fi 802.11ac standard used in many modern routers employs beamforming to improve reception. To maximize probability of target detection in airborne antenna radar, linear filters (e.g., Wiener) and nonlinear filters are used for space-time adaptive processing (STAP) to reduce noise and clutter. Machine learning using an ANN supports parallel, distributed, and adaptive processing, and noise reduction [10]. Multipath fading using ML supports analysis in complex scenarios [11]. Recent results using deep learning have demonstrated clutter suppression to improve target detection over STAP methods [12].

With the prevalence of big data from IoT systems such as phones, appliances, drones, traffic lights, security systems, and environmental sensors, there now is a need to apply deep learning (DL) to RF signals. ML provides dimension reduction, data classification, and pattern recognition. Deep learning applied to the RF spectrum could understand the composition of the RF spectrum–discerning the kinds of signals occupying it, differentiating those that are important from the background, and identifying those that don't follow the rules. Hence, DL would enable robust RF performance in complex scenarios.

According to the Defense Advanced Research Project Agency (DARPA) radio frequency machine learning systems (RFMLS) program [13], there is power in utilizing ML techniques to enhance RF radar, communication, and control technology. Examples include the ability to:

- Discern subtle but inevitable differences in the RF signals from what otherwise are identical [14] and to distinguish these from signals intended to spoof or hack into these devices [15];
- Understand and trust what is happening in the Internet of Things and to stand up an RF forensics capability to identify unique and peculiar signals amongst the mix of signals [16];
- Recognize a specific transmitter based on the unique RF fingerprint naturally imparted by hardware imperfections within that transmitter [17];
- Provide spectrum awareness from narrow to wide bandwidths amongst software defined radios, spectrum sharing, and other signals for communication and navigation [18];
- Modify transmit waveforms to enhance robust sensing and communication [19].

Combining deep learning (cognition) with RF signals analysis has benefits of:

- *Feature learning:* Identify and characterize RF signals in various settings. An example is detecting signal strength variations to determine the presence/absence of jamming.
- *Salient attention:* Direct attention to what is potentially important in the RF spectrum in which it is operating. An example is determining a signal of interest of a communications signal in a frequency band usually devoted to radar signals.
- *Sensor configuration:* Tune receiver locations and receptivity to signals and features the systems deem to be most effective at accomplishing the task at hand. An example is automatically placing the antennas and power selections to maximize target detection.
- *Waveform/signal synthesis:* Synthesize waveforms tailored to the specific RF devices they emanate to give sophisticated radios for improved identify verification. An example is in a crowded and adversarial spectrum, the opportunity to generate and discriminate the particular digital waveforms that increase performance.

With the many options to improve RF signals analysis for sensing, communication, and navigation, the next sections review these concepts towards deep-learning applications. Section 2.2 reviews communications signals with details on analog and digital modulation, shift keying for digital communications, and wireless technology. Section 2.3 describes three types of deep-learning methods for RF signals including (1) channel analysis, (2) I/Q imbalance, and (3) emitter analysis. Section 2.4 provides a discussion and Section 2.5 conclusions.

2.2 Communication Channels

The objective of a RF communication system is to move data or messages from one location (source) to another location (destination). The source and destination are connected by a communication channel. A communication channel can be a physical medium (such as a cable connecting two computers) or a wireless channel (such as Wi-Fi). To send data, the source uses a transmitter (Tx); and similarly, to receive the data, the destination employs a receiver (Rx) to process and understand the data. Figure 2.2 is a simple block diagram of a digital spread spectrum (SS) RF communication system. SS RF communications are important as the narrowband signal is spread in the frequency domain to enhance a wider bandwidth, giving communications benefits such as: (a) secure transmission (e.g., utilize frequency hopping), (b) resilient detection (e.g., mitigate adversarial jamming), (c) robust performance (e.g., operate in presence of interference and noise), (d) limited power (e.g., in satellite down links), and (e) increased users (e.g., enabling multiple-access).

All digital communication systems have a block diagram like that in Figure 2.2; however, they differ from each other primarily on spreading approaches and modulation schemes employed for data transmission and reception in RF systems. Modulation, along with bandwidth and frequency technologies, has an impact on data rate, bit error rate, signal security, signal interference, and overall systems complexity. To increase the channel capacity, RF communications systems utilize diversity over: (a) *spatial diversity*: multiple (ground, air, space) mobile of base stations, (b) *frequency diversity*: more than one carrier frequency is used, (c) *time diversity*: information is sent with time spacings, and (d) *polarization*: orthogonal polarization of signal. The next sections overview analog and digital signals modulation fundamentals that are utilized in contemporary DL RF approaches.

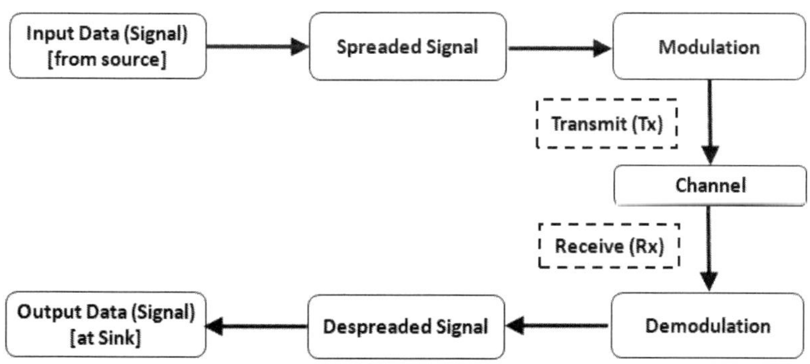

Figure 2.2
Block diagram of a spread spectrum communication system.

2.3 RF Signals Analysis

For RF wireless transmission of a signal as an electromagnetic wave, the system is allocated a certain bandwidth around a carrier frequency as shown in Figure 2.3. The RF systems operate within a passband that spans a particular bandwidth (B), that is centered about a particular passband frequency (f_c). Thus, an analog stream of signals (or digital stream of information bits) is upconverted to a passband frequency within the allocated bandwidth. *Passband signals* are determined by the shift of the baseband signal, and once that spectrum (B) is occupied, no other entity can share the channel for the purpose of communications. Hence, everyday RF communication uses FM radio, Wi-Fi, cellular (i.e., 4G and 5G), and Bluetooth, which are all passband signals that execute transmission within their respective frequency bands sharing the same physical medium [20]. To shift the spectrum to a designated carrier frequency is accomplished by multiplying, or mixing, it with a sinusoidal waveform, as show in Figure 2.3. Note that:

- In time domain, a pulse amplitude modulation waveform can be multiplied with a carrier sinusoid at frequency f_c.
- Time domain multiplication between two signals is frequency domain convolution between their spectra.
- The spectrum of a pure sinusoid at any frequency is composed of two impulses at that frequency.

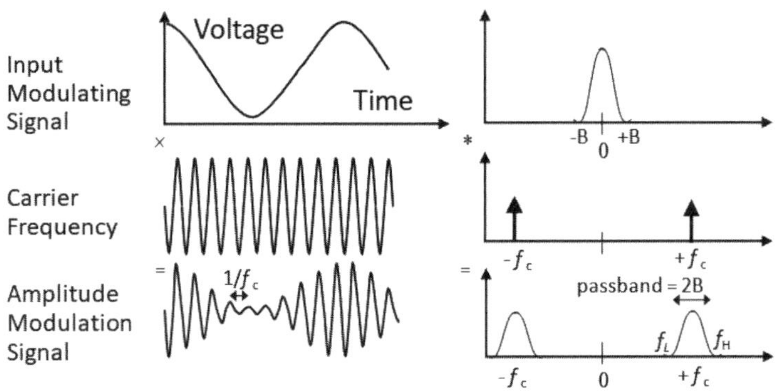

Figure 2.3
Passband signal.

- The convolution of a signal with a unit impulse results in the same signal parked at its allocated slot.

The resulting passband waveform propagates through the RF environment, which is typically called the *channel* for the purposes of RF communications analysis. The communications receiver transduces the RF waveform at the receiver antenna front end, and the resulting signal waveform is typically not identical to that which was transmitted from the sender.

One difference between the transmitted signal waveform and that which enters the receiver front end is that the *multipath and fading effects* can be present in the intervening channel. Often, it is possible to assume that most of these effects depend linearly on the transmitted signal, so that a communications channel can be modeled according to an impulse response function $h(t)$ of time. The response function gives the received waveform due to a transmitted signal that is an impulse function that is nonzero only at $t = 0$ and is zero for $t \neq 0$. Thus, if a general passband signal waveform $x(t)$ is transmitted through a channel that is modeled by the impulse response $h(t)$, which characterizes the multipath and fading channel effects, then the signal waveform at the front end of the receiver $y(t)$ is given by:

$$y(t) = h(t) \ast x(t) \tag{2.1}$$

That is, the physical effects of multipath and fading depend upon the actual signal that was transmitted according to a one-dimensional convolution $\ast$ in time with the impulse response $h(t)$ of the channel.

The signal at the receiver front end can include other signals emanating from the local environment, including both intentional and unintentional inference sources. These *interference sources* are typically modeled as an additive contribution relative to the convolutional channel response of (2.1). In addition, thermal noise effects can also be present in the receiver front end, which results from noise that is generated within the receiver electronics components themselves. These sources of noise, intentional interference and unintentional interference, are collectively modeled according to the function $n(t)$ of time. Thus, the overall communications system model is assumed to comply with the standard linear form used for analysis of received signals in complicated multipath, fading, and nonuniform noise environments (e.g., [21–25]):

$$y(t) = h(t) \ast x(t) + n(t) \tag{2.2}$$

Analogously, in the frequency domain:

$$Y(f) = H(f)F(f) + N(f) \tag{2.3}$$

And for digital systems:

$$\mathbf{y}_c(n) = \mathbf{H}\mathbf{x}(n) + \mathbf{n}_b(n) \tag{2.4}$$

where

$\mathbf{H} = [\mathbf{h}(\theta_0), \ldots, \mathbf{h}(\theta_{L-1})]$	a $D \times L$ array steering matrix
$\mathbf{x}(n) = [\mathbf{r}_1(0), \ldots, \mathbf{r}_L(N-1)]$	a $L \times N$ array steering matrix
$\mathbf{n}_b(n) = [\mathbf{n}(0), \ldots, \mathbf{n}(N-1)]$	a complex Gaussian noise matrix $N(0, \mathbf{I}\sigma^2)$

with θ as the direction of arrival angle. The baseband sinusoidal signal $s(t)$ is convenient for understanding the fundamentals of communications modulation and demodulation, and is expressed as:

$$s(t) = A(t)\cos(\theta(t)) \tag{2.5}$$

where $A(t)$ is the time-varying amplitude and $\theta(t)$ is the time-varying angle. For the case in which the phase function has the form $\theta(t) = \omega_c(t) + \alpha(t)$, (2.5) can be written as:

$$s(t) = A(t)\cos\left[\omega_c(t) + \alpha(t)\right] \tag{2.6}$$

where $\omega_c(t)$ is the carrier frequency and $\alpha(t)$ is the phase modulation. Often, $a(t)$ is called the envelope of the signal $s(t)$. At a fixed, t, then the sine wave is represented as:

$$s(t) = A_c \cos\left[2\pi f_c t + \phi\right] \tag{2.7}$$

where the angle θ is represented as the frequency (f) and phase (ϕ).

2.4 RF Analog Signals Modulation

Some common modulation techniques are amplitude modulation (AM), frequency modulation (FM), phase modulation (PM), and pulse modulation (PuM). For convenience, Figure 2.4 presents both the analog and digital modulation methods.

In *amplitude modulation*, the phase of the signal $\alpha(t)$ is kept constant while envelope can be changed in proportional to the modulating signal $f(t)$. Hence, an amplitude modulated signal can be written as:

$$s_{am}(t) = f(t)\cos\left(\omega_c(t)\right) \tag{2.8}$$

Within AM, there are techniques called AM with double-sideband suppressed carrier (DSB-SC), and AM with double-sideband

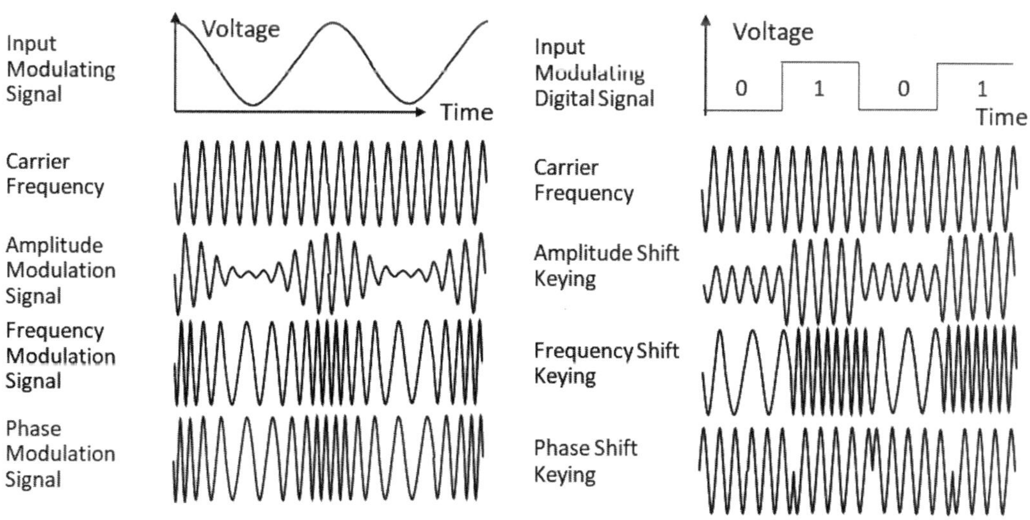

Figure 2.4
Signal modulation and shift keying over amplitude, frequency, and phase.

large carrier (DSB-LC). DSB signals can be converted to single sideband (SSB) to use a particular band efficiently. Vestigial sideband (VSB) is a modulation scheme that is used to mitigate issues with SSB or DSB modulation. In *frequency modulation*, the amplitude $a(t)$ is kept constant while the frequency $\omega_c(t)$ can be varied in proportion to the modulating signal $f(t)$. For the case of FM modulation, there are narrowband FM and wideband FM signals. In phase modulation, the phase is varied in proportion to the modulating signal $f(t)$. In pulse-amplitude modulation (PAM), the amplitude of constant with pulses are changed in proportion to the sample values of the modulating signal. Among various types of pulse modulations, pulse position modulation (PPM), pulse code modulation (PCM), and pulse width modulation (PWM) are also commonly used in communication systems.

2.5 RF Digital Signals Modulation

For digital communication, if there are different *spreading sequences*, then the system modulates the carrier signal with digital data (input) and then performs data transmission. The different dimensions over which modulation is performed to separate signals in frequency (FDMA), time (TDMA), and code division multiple access (CDMA) [26], as well as wireless standards orthogonal frequency division multiple access (OFDMA), as shown in Figure 2.5. Current techniques include OFDMA [27] and wideband CDMA (WCDMA). From these methods, the types of modulation are frequency (FM), amplitude (AM), and phase (PM) modulation.

Correspondingly, the modulation of digital data can be decomposed into keys using shifting approaches. Figure 2.6 illustrates the key assignment of 1s and 0s based on the shifts in the signal amplitude and phase. These approaches include amplitude-shift keying (ASK), frequency-shift keying (FSK), phase-shift keying (PSK), and their combinations. Several other important modulations are quadrature amplitude modulation (QAM), quaternary PSK (QPSK), M-symbol orthogonal FSK, and amplitude phase keying (APK). Each of these modulation techniques have advantages and disadvantages in terms of bit error rate and bandwidth efficiency. Among the variations of PSK, binary PSK (BPSK), and differential PSK (DPSK) are most commonly used. For example, in direct sequence

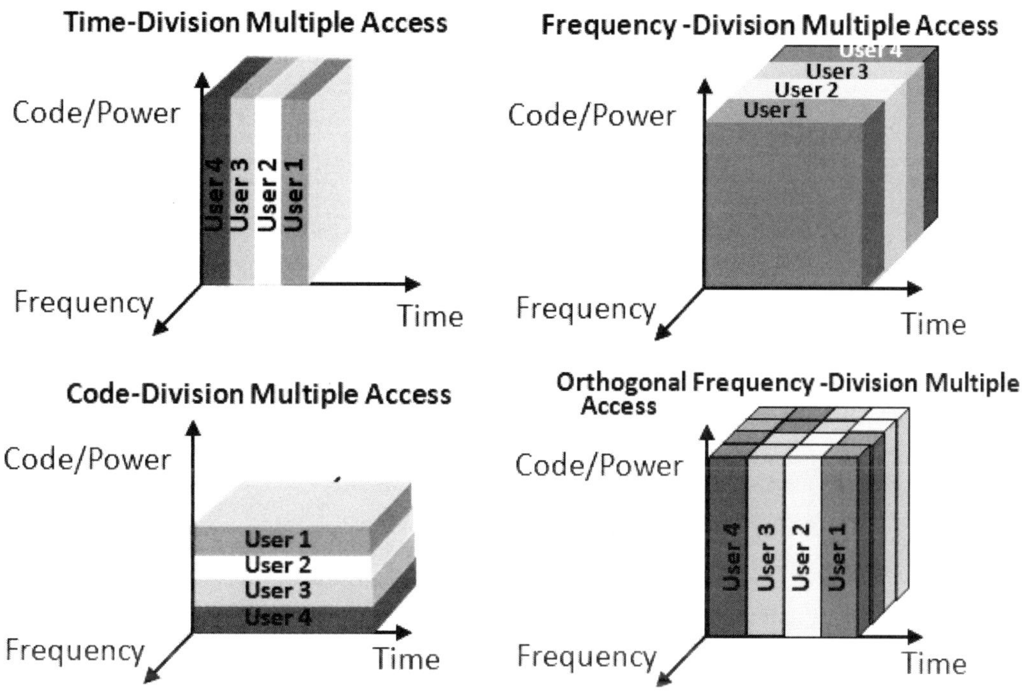

Figure 2.5
Partition-based multiple access strategies, including division, among users based upon slots in time, frequency, and spreading code.

spread spectrum (DSSS), BPSK modulation is used. A DSSS system allows code division multiple access (CDMA) that reduces interference among users, and hence is an important technique for satellite [28, 29] and avionic [30] communication systems. The CDMA transmitter architecture is shown in Figure 2.6. To transmit a digital message over a wireless spectrum, baseband digital up conversion of the digital data is needed, which is achieved with shift keying, presented in the next section.

2.6 RF Shift Keying

Many communications systems apply *phase shift keying* (PSK), in which different phases (ϕ) within the in-phase (I) and quadrature (Q) contributions of the modulation and demodulation processes are used to send a number of symbols across a communications

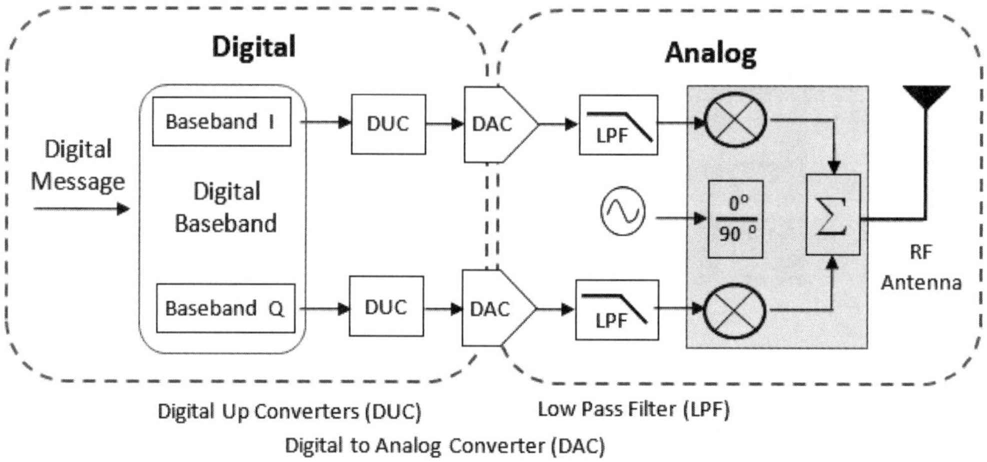

Figure 2.6
Interim Standard 95 (IS-95) transceiver for cellular CDMA.

channel. Note, from Figure 2.7, that Q and I signals have the same frequency but are different in phase by 90°. PSK can be used with any number of phase values with a corresponding number of possible symbols. The only requirement is that the sender and receiver both agree on the selected mapping. For example, binary phase shift keying applies the two-phase values of {0°, 180°}. Quadrature phase shift keying uses the four phases {0°, 90°, 180°, 270°}, as demonstrated in Figure 2.7.

The notation N-PSK conveys the general transmission of N symbols via an equal number of possible phase values. For example, 8-PSK uses eight different phase values $\alpha(t) = 0°, 45°, 90°, 135°, 180°,$

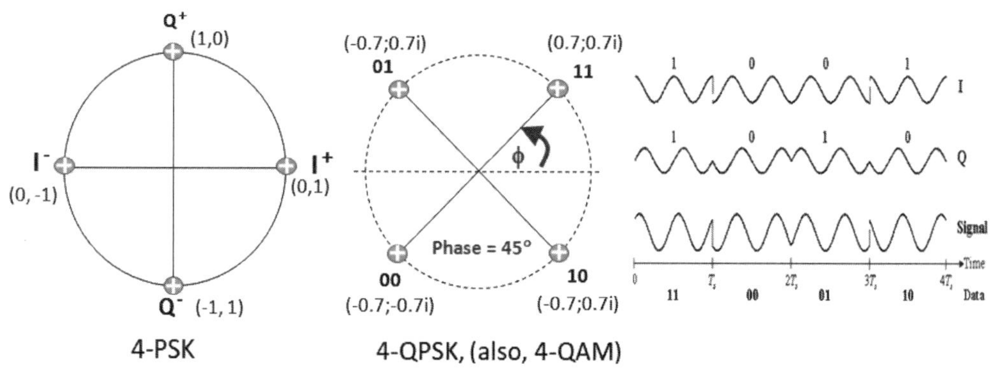

Figure 2.7
Four-phase shift keying and quadrature amplitude modulation.

225°, 270°, 315° in sending a single symbol from the transmitter to the receiver to achieve eight different data symbols. For 8-PSK modulation, each symbol conveys three bits of information, corresponding to the $2^3 = 8$ different phase values. Specifically, it is possible to define the following bit sequences corresponding to each of phase values: $\{0° \Rightarrow 0\ 0\ 0\}$, $\{45° \Rightarrow 0\ 0\ 1\}$, $\{90° \Rightarrow 0\ 1\ 0\}$, $\{135° \Rightarrow 0\ 1\ 1\}$, $\{180° \Rightarrow 1\ 0\ 0\}$, $\{225° \Rightarrow 1\ 0\ 1\}$, $\{270° \Rightarrow 1\ 1\ 0\}$, and $\{315° \Rightarrow 1\ 1\ 1\}$. This choice of mapping between a given 8-PSK symbol and the corresponding sequence of three bits is not unique. That is, other mappings can be selected arbitrarily.

Another form of modulation/demodulation is based upon *frequency shift keying*, where a communications system can employ a number of frequency slots for sending symbols from one node to another. For example, suppose that a communications system that spans the frequencies between 30 to 41 MHz is allocated into frequency slots with the following minimum and maximum frequencies (in megahertz): $\{30 \rightarrow 32\}$, $\{33 \rightarrow 35\}$, $\{36 \rightarrow 38\}$, and $\{39 \rightarrow 41\}$. Each of the four selected frequency subbands in this example are separated by a 1-MHz guard band, to mitigate the effects of interference between adjacent channels. The corresponding center frequencies of each of these bands is given by {31, 34, 37, 40} MHz. Each of the center frequencies can be selected to map to a set of $2^2 = 4$ different sequences of 2 bits each. One possible mapping between center frequencies and corresponding bit sequences is the following: $\{31\text{ MHz} \Rightarrow 0\ 0\}$, $\{34\text{ MHz} \Rightarrow 0\ 1\}$,$\{37\text{ MIIz} \Rightarrow 1\ 0\}$, $\{40\text{ MHz} \Rightarrow 1\ 1\}$. As with the PSK example, the mapping between frequency symbols and bit sequences is not unique, it is only necessary for the transmitter and receiver to agree on the mapping prior to the transmission of any frequency symbols.

Another widely used mode of modulation/demodulation scheme is *quadrature amplitude modulation*, in which both the amplitude $a(t)$ and phase $\alpha(t)$ are modulated simultaneously to send symbols over a transmission channel. QAM yields a specific set of symbols on the constellation diagram that is comprised of the *I value* of a given symbol, as determined by the horizontal axis, and the *Q value* of the symbol plotted along the vertical axis. Thus, for QAM modulation/demodulation, there are a number of symbols on the I-Q constellation diagram that form a rectangular grid of symbols equally spaced along both the horizontal and vertical directions. Common implementations of QAM include QAM-16 (with a rectangular grid of 4 × 4 symbols, shown in Figure 2.8), QAM-64 (8 × 8 symbols), and QAM-256 (16 × 16 symbols).

To implement QAM, I/Q modulators generate RF signals from baseband information for digital communication systems. The I/Q data resulting from sampling of a signal allows all the amplitude, frequency, and phase information contained in the signal to be preserved. From (2.7), the I/Q signals are determined from:

$$I(t) = A(t)\cos(\phi(t)) \tag{2.9}$$

$$Q(t) = A(t)\sin(\phi(t)) \tag{2.10}$$

To accurately analyze or demodulate the signal in different ways, the two double-balanced mixers combine the I/Q signals. By targeting specific points in amplitude and phase, high-order modulation is created. For example, from Figure 2.8, with 16-QAM, each symbol can convey four bits of information [31]. Virtually any type of RF modulation can be generated with I/Q modulation, within the center frequency, bandwidth, and accuracy capabilities of the

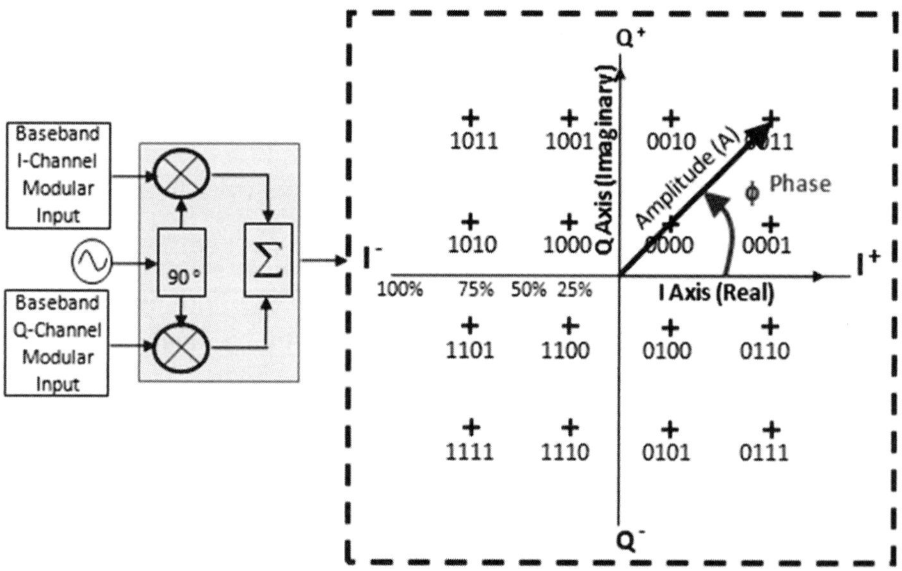

Figure 2.8
Sixteen-quadrature amplitude modulation.

modulator device. Hence, the I/Q data produced from the modulator provides information for deep learning applications.

2.7 RF Wi-Fi

One type of RF signal that is becoming ubiquitous in urban environments is *Wi-Fi 802.11*, due to its prevalent use in wireless networks that use the standard transport control protocol (TCP)/ Internet Protocol (IP) suite of the open internet. Most implementations of Wi-Fi apply a strategy for sharing spectrum among many users that is based upon *orthogonal frequency division multiplexing* (see Figure 2.5). The OFDM multiplexing scheme applies multiple orthogonal subcarrier signals that have overlapping spectral properties. For example, the OFDM transmitter (Figure 2.9) employs QAM modulation to support the digital conversion of signals for RF transmission. Likewise, the receiver of a given subcarrier signal can be extracted with minimal interference from the other orthogonal subcarrier signals. OFDM is well-suited for environments with strong fading and multipath due to complicated channel conditions wherein many users can be packed into the RF channel. Then, each subcarrier can be modulated using PSK or QAM to carry the actual information symbols over the channel.

Another issue mentioned here is that most communications systems favor frequency-division multiple access (FDMA), as with OFDMA for Wi-Fi signals, over CDMA that was applied in earlier

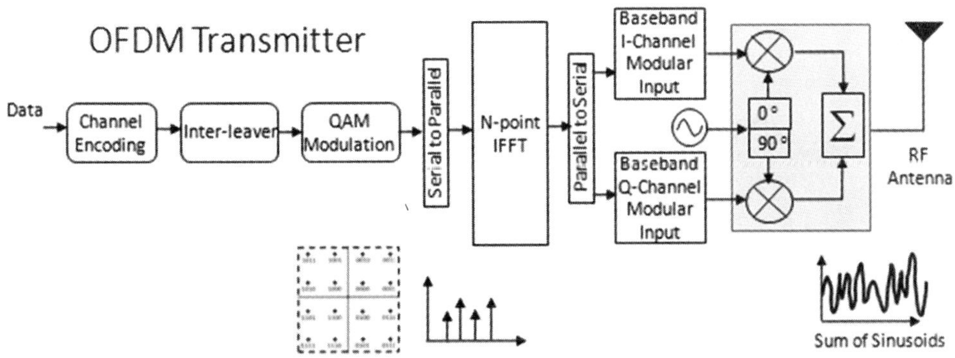

Figure 2.9
OFDM transmitter.

generations of communications systems, shown in Figure 2.10 [32]. The use of FDMA for wireless 4G follows a trend that is expected to continue in order to improve susceptibility to interference and pack many different users in a very dense and contested communications environment.

Figure 2.10 describes the three common types of partitioning of a channel amongst several users. However, Wi-Fi 802.11 does not use channel partitioning. Instead, it uses a shared access protocol strategy referred to as *carrier sense multiple access with collision avoidance.* When multiple users try to utilize a common RF communications channel, collisions can occur between two different transmitters that are attempting to transmit their RF symbols simultaneously. For such scenarios, it is likely that the current demodulation of the intended symbols will lead to high error rates so that the overall attempted communications fail. Thus, it is necessary for the network to be able to deal with such multiple users with CSMA/CA.

Typically, in CSMA/CA a request to send (RTS) and clear to send (CTS) messages are transmitted in order to reduce the probability of collisions occurring within this contentious RF transmission environment, as shown in Figure 2.11 [33]. CSMA/CA is necessary to deal with the reality that mobile phone antennas are small and transmit with weak effective radiative power (ERP), whereas the base stations and wireless access points typically have higher ERP. Thus, each of two different mobile phones in a particular scenario may be able to detect and communicate with the WAP, but they may not be able to detect each other. When two devices cannot detect

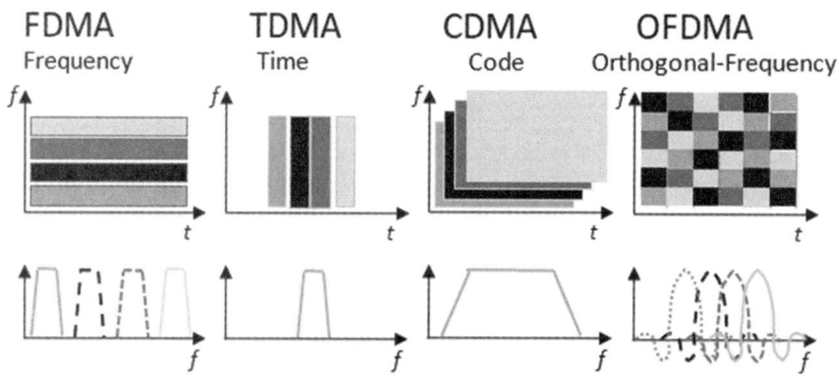

Figure 2.10
Multiple access methods.

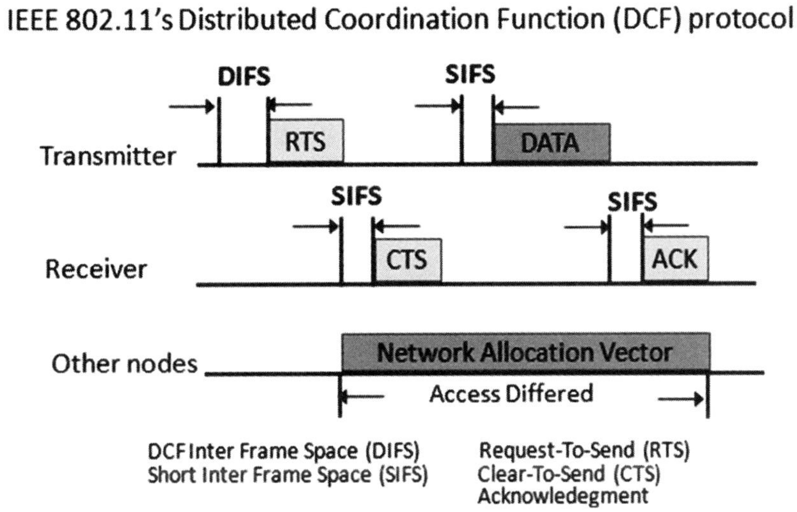

Figure 2.11
Carrier sense multiple access with collision avoidance protocol.

each other, it leads to the hidden node problem wherein the individual mobile phones are unaware of transmissions of the other and thus are required to rely upon WAP coordination via RTS and CTS message to maintain proper communications in a contentious environment. Given the approaches for signal transmission for communication, then the utility of ML is in signal detection.

2.8 RF Signal Detection

The *first step* in processing the *receiver front end* is to down-convert the input signal $y(t) = h(t) \ast x(t) + n(t)$ to a lower frequency, either at an intermediate frequency or *signal baseband*. For the convenience of discussion, assume that all signals entering the receiver antenna are downconverted to baseband before the ML algorithms are applied. The basic reason for choosing the downconverted signals is to reduce the size of the input data sets and corresponding requirements applied to the input and storage of signal data sets. That is, the Nyquist theorem requires that the signal must be sampled at a frequency that is no lower than twice that of the maximum frequency of the underlying signal in order to accurately reproduce the original analogue signal. A signal at baseband typically requires far fewer total samples of the signal waveform than the corresponding waveform at its original passband frequency, often by a factor of 10 or more. However, ML algorithms could be applied to intermediate or passband frequencies, as in the case of *software defined radios* (SDRs), wherein the full passband signal can be sampled.

Multiple methods can be applied to detect and estimate desired signals for such nonideal collection conditions. For example, mobile phones and other communications systems can use *rake receivers* and adaptive frequency allocation, as is applied with 4G FDMA [34]. The ability of the receiver to obtain accurate estimates of the transmitted symbols depends primarily upon the signal to interference plus noise ratio (SINR). Thus, there exist straightforward methods to demodulate signals in order to generate accurate estimates of the transmitted signals, provided that the SINR is sufficiently high. However, the ability to distinguish one emitter from another, in the absence of cooperative information, is quite a difficult problem in general. Traditional ML approaches use the SVM, AdaBoost, and least squares SVM (LS-SVM) that were applied to the phase data φ as the signal weights [35]. The signal-to-interference ratio was used in the ML analysis to update the rake receivers, as shown in Figure 2.12.

For problem elements that are relatively well understood and straightforward, as with the modulation and demodulation of communications symbols, standard methods are applied that do not use or invoke ML methods. However, for problem elements that are exceptionally difficult and are poorly understood, as with the noncooperative classification and identification of communications transmitters, then ML techniques can enhance performance. That is, for parts of the overall signals classification that are described accurately using a particular physics-based mathematical model, then understanding how to predict or estimate those particular elements of the problem for accurate models exists. In contrast, for problem elements that are fundamentally an enigma, or for which the understanding is more art than science, then ML should be applied. Therefore, a reasonable approach to solving the problem of identifying a transmitter's manufacturer or identification is to apply ML methods. To determine the transmitter function, an equivalent knowledge of the receiver is needed, as shown in Figure 2.13.

The signal observed is a function of the real-world physical transmitting and receiving communications systems, as opposed to

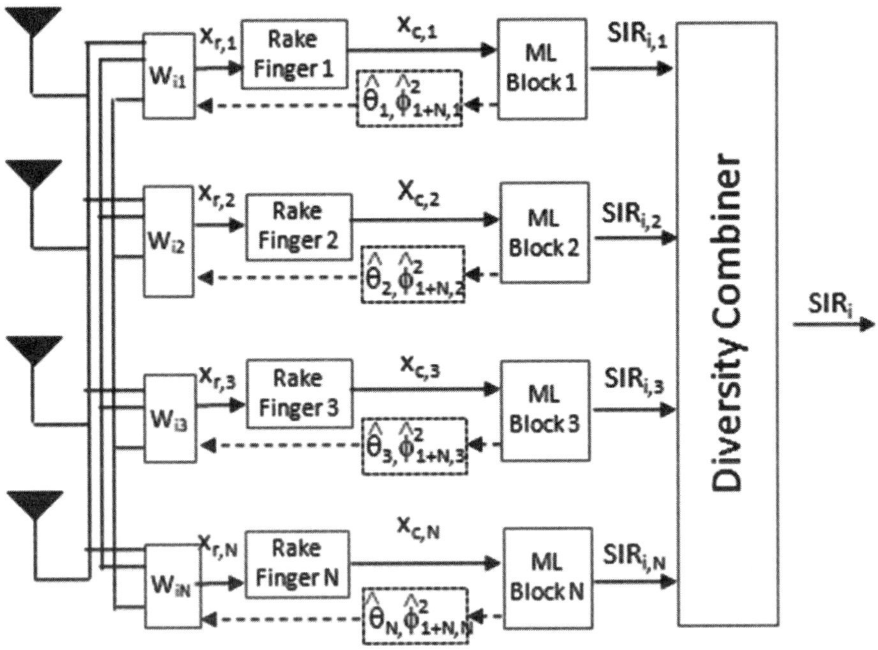

Figure 2.12
CDMA power control and direction of arrival estimation using ML.

the idealized communications devices invoked in theoretical analyses. Specifically, theoretic analyses often assume that the transmitted signal waveform exhibits perfect quality with respect to amplitude $a(t)$, frequency $\omega_c(t)$, and phase $\alpha(t)$. That is, symbols are transmitted according to the theoretic analytic equations, with infinitely sharp temporal transitions of $\{a(t), \omega_c(t), \alpha(t)\}$, according to the modulation type. For example, with theoretically idealized amplitude modulation, the amplitude $a(t)$ changes instantaneously in time, from one amplitude value to a different value corresponding to the transition from one symbol to the next.

In contrast, real physical transmitting devices exhibit small deviations in the signal amplitude $a(t)$, frequency $\omega_c(t)$, and phase $\alpha(t)$ away from the functional forms that are expected. That is, for physically realistic transmitters with actual circuit elements used to generate the transmitted signal, the amplitude does not change instantaneously, but primarily occurs over a smaller, albeit nonzero, interval in time. In addition, the rapid symbol transition can occur with a relatively unique shape of the signal which is dependent

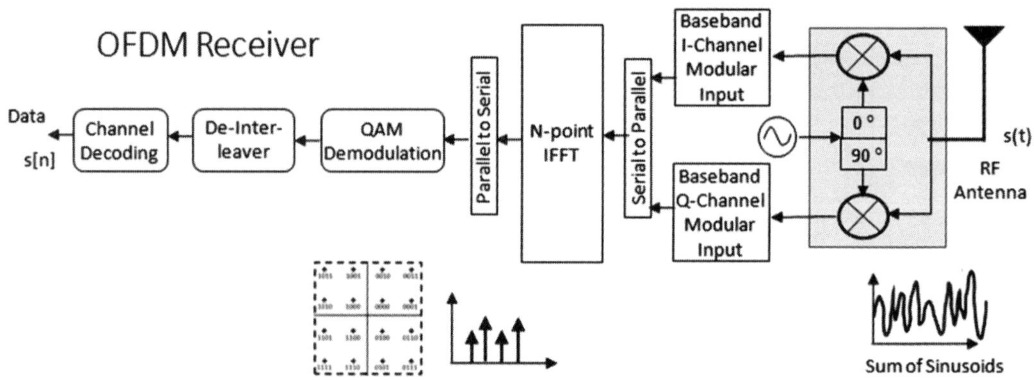

Figure 2.13
OFDM receiver.

upon the actual circuit elements selected in the fabrication process. Of course, each manufacturer is free to design a unique configuration of circuit elements that generates the required transmission signals and receives them at the other end of the channel. These circuit differences can yield small differences in the resulting communications waveforms.

With the imprecision of *timing transitions* due to hardware components, the same basic concepts apply to frequency modulation, phase modulation, or any combinations of these modulation approaches. The frequency cannot change instantaneously from one symbol to another but instead occurs over a small but nonzero interval in time. Furthermore, the shape of the signal for the generation of one symbol transitioning to another can be different when comparing two different manufacturers. Thus, a potentially unique signal shape can provide a type of signature for the classification and identification of RF emitters. These same concepts apply to *phase transitions* as well because the signal phase cannot change instantaneously in time from one symbol to another. In addition, these issues apply to all generic modulations that can involve the encoding of information via the intended variations in signal amplitude $a(t)$, frequency $\omega_c(t)$, and phase $\alpha(t)$, as is desired to occur with the convenient theoretic ideals of signal generation and reception. The unintended component is the residual signal component that is not present in the theoretical models. These signal contributions are difficult to understand via physical models and thus are good candidates to benefit from ML methods. Thus, these unintended signal variations are effectively the small subtle signal components that are being sought for exploitation via ML.

2.9 Conclusions

This chapter set the foundation for the use of ML to classify RF communication signals. It discussed how ML can be used for developing a cognitive RF system that provides software signal processing, analysis of received signals analysis, and hardware emitter classification. In the next chapter, we shall examine issues involved in the collection of RF signals.

References

[1] Liang, P., et al., "Multiple Kernel Learning for Vehicle Detection in Wide Area Motion Imagery," *International Conference on Information Fusion*, Singapore, 2012.

[2] McConaghy, T., et al., "Classification of Audio Radar Signals Using Radial Basis Function Neural Networks," *IEEE Transactions on Instrumentation and Measurement*, Vol. 52, No. 6, 2003, pp. 1771–1779.

[3] Falcon, R., Abielmona, R., and Blasch, E., "Behavioral Learning of Vessel Types with Fuzzy-Rough Decision Trees," *International Conference on Information Fusion*, Salamanca, Spain, 2014.

[4] Malec, M., et al., "Inductive Logic Programming Meets Relational Databases: An Application to Statistical Relational Learning," *Sixth International Workshop on Statistical Relational AI (StarAI) Workshop*, New York City, 2016.

[5] Falcon, R., Abielmona, R., and Blasch, E., "Behavioral Learning of Vessel Types with Fuzzy-Rough Decision Trees," *International Conference on Information Fusion*, Salamanca, Spain, 2014.

[6] Lu, J., et al., "Machine Learning-Based Intelligent Cognitive Network Using Fog Computing," *Proc. SPIE*, Vol. 10196, 2017.

[7] Blasch, E., et al., "Trends in Survivable/Secure Cognitive Networks," *IEEE International Conference on Computing, Networking, and Communications*, San Diego, CA, January 2013.

[8] Guerci, J. R., et al., "CoFAR: Cognitive Fully Adaptive Radar," *IEEE Radar Conference*, Cincinnati, OH, 2014.

[9] Xiong, W., et al., "Cognitive Radio Testbed for Digital Beamforming of Satellite Communication," *Cognitive Communications for Aerospace Applications Workshop (CCAA)*, Cleveland, OH, 2017.

[10] Johnson, J., et al., "Learning Algorithms for Suppressing Motion Clutter in Airborne Array Radar," *IEEE National Aerospace and Electronics Conference*, Dayton, OH, 1997, pp. 840–845.

[11] Wang, R., et al., "Intelligent Path Loss Prediction Engine Design Using Machine Learning in the Urban Outdoor Environment," *Proc. SPIE*, 2018, Vol. 10641, pp. 160–166.

[12] Zhang, Q., et al., "Novel Method for Sea Clutter Suppression and Target Detection Via Deep Convolutional Autoencoder," *International Journal of Signal Processing*, Vol. 2, 2017, pp. 35–40.

[13] https://www.darpa.mil/program/radio-frequency-machine-learning-systems.

[14] Yang, C., Nguyen, T., and Blasch, E., "Mobile Positioning Via Fusion of Mixed Signals of Opportunity," *IEEE Aerospace and Electronic Systems Magazine*, Vol. 29, No. 4, April 2014, pp. 34–46.

[15] Shafiee, E., Mosavi, M. R., and Moazedi, M., "Detection of Spoofing Attack Using Machine Learning Based on Multi-Layer Neural Network in Single-Frequency GPS Receivers," *The Journal of Navigation*, Vol. 71, No. 1, 2018, pp. 169–188.

[16] Nagothu, D., et al., "Detecting Malicious False Frame Injection Attacks on Surveillance Systems at the Edge Using Electrical Network Frequency Signals," *Sensors*, Vol, 19, No. 11, 2019, p. 2424.

[17] Roy, D., et al., "RFAL: Adversarial Learning for RF Transmitter Identification and Classification," *IEEE Transactions on Cognitive Communications and Networking*, October 2019.

[18] Mukherjee, T., et al., "LoSI: Large Scale Location Inference Through FM Signal Integration and Estimation," *Big Data Mining and Analytics*, Vol. 2, No. 4, December 2019, pp. 319–348.

[19] Sira, S. P., et al., "Waveform-Agile Sensing for Tracking," *IEEE Signal Processing Magazine*, Vol. 26, No. 1, January 2009, pp. 53–64.

[20] Chaudhari, Q., "Wireless Pi," https://wirelesspi.com/quadrature-amplitude-modulation-qam/.

[21] Guerci, J. R., "Optimum Matched Illumination-Reception Radar for Target Classification," U.S. Patent 5,381,154, 1995.

[22] Pillai, S. U., et al., "Optimum Transmit-Receiver Design in the Presence of Signal-Dependent Interference and Channel Noise," in *IEEE Transactions on Information Theory*, Vol. 46, No. 2, March 2000.

[23] Garren, D. A., et al., "Optimal Transmission Pulse Shape for Detection and Identification with Uncertain Target Aspect," *IEEE Radar Conference*, May 2001, pp. 123–128.

[24] Garren, D. A., et al., "Enhanced Target Detection and Identification Via Optimized Radar Transmission Pulse Shape," *Proceedings of Radar, Sonar & Navigation*, Vol. 148, No. 3, June 2001, pp. 130–138.

[25] Garren, D. A., et al., "Full-Polarization Matched-Illumination for Target Detection and Identification," *IEEE Transactions on Aerospace and Electronic Systems*, Vol. 38, Issue 3, December 2002, pp. 824–837.

[26] Vanhi, V., Damnjanovic, A., and Vojcic, B., *The cdma2000 System for Mobile Communications*, Hoboken, NJ: Prentice Hall, 2004.

[27] Chen, Y., et al., "Towards the Standardization of Non-orthogonal Multiple Access for Next Generation Wireless Networks," *IEEE Communications Magazine*, Vol. 56, No. 3, March 2018, pp. 19–27.

[28] Wang, G., et al., "Performance Evaluation of SATCOM Link in the Presence of Radio Frequency Interference," *IEEE Aerospace*, 2016.

[29] Wang, G., et al., "Spread Spectrum Design for Aeronautical Communication Systems with Radio Frequency Interference," *IEEE/AIAA Digital Avionics Systems Conference*, 2015.

[30] Xiong, W., et al., "Distributed Coherent MIMO System with Advanced CDMA Channel Estimation," *IEEE Aerospace*, 2017.

[31] Hemp, B., and Hsiao, S., "Low Power IQ Modulator for Digital Communications," *Analog Devices*, accessed at https://www.analog.com/en/technical-articles/low-power-iq-modulator-for-digital-communications.html.

[32] Iannacci, J., "The Future 5th Generation (5G) of Mobile Networks: Challenges and Opportunities of an Impelling Scenario," Chapter 3 in *RF-MEMS Technology for High-Performance Passives*, J. Iannacci (ed.), IOP Publishing Ltd., 2017.

[33] Sharma, R., et al., "A Survey of MAC Layer Protocols to Avoid Deafness in Wireless Networks Using Directional Antenna," Chapter 19 in *Mobile Computing and Wireless Networks: Concepts, Methodologies, Tools, and Applications*, R. Sharma, G. R. Kadambi, Y. Vershinin, and K. N. Mukundan (eds.), 2014.

[34] Chandrasekhar, V., Livingston, R., and Cavallaro, J. R., "Reducing Dynamic Power Consumption in Next Generation DS-CDMA Mobile Communication Receivers," *Proc. of International Conference on Application-Specific Systems, Architectures and Processors*, Vol. 3, No. 3, 2003, pp. 260–270.

[35] Rohwer, J. A., "Machine Learning Methods for CDMA Power Control and Direction of Arrival Estimation," PhD dissertation, Univ. of New Mexico, 2003.

3

Access to RF Signals

3.1 Introduction

This chapter presents methodologies for RF signals collections from various locations. RF signals collection results from stationary and mobile platforms operating in ground, air, or space domains. Each RF collection method requires geometrical knowledge between the source and target, electrical understanding of the power and wavelength availability, and the mechanical attributes of the size and weight. Together, the size, weight, and power (SWAP) are key elements determining the quality of the signal collection.

An essential component of RF signals collection is from space platforms. Hence, it is important to know satellite orbits, locations, and communication capabilities, as well as the merits and limitations of strategic RF signals collection from space. Depending on the applications, a satellite (i.e., RF collector) can be installed very close or far away from the Earth's surface.

The rest of the chapter describes RF signal collection platforms and attributes of signals collections from the space environment. There is a review of the basic concepts necessary to consider when analyzing RF collections. The key elements include: (1) domain of collection (i.e., space, air, ground), (2) strength of collection (e.g., size, weight, and power), and (3) RF signal types.

3.2 RF Signal Collection Platforms

Various platforms are used to transmit and receive RF signals. Often space-based platforms are active sources of transmission, and ground, water, air, and space systems serve as the receiver. Ground, water, or air platforms can also be used as the RF emitters. There can be multiple combinations of transmit and receive sources comprising space, air, ground, and air platforms. This section provides an overview of signal collections by various countries. The information provided here is from freely available online sources and introduces the readers to various collections platforms, and encourages them to seek additional information for specific details. The locations of the collection platforms by country are found in open sources and cannot be verified [1]. Figure 3.1 summarizes the radar and communications bands and their common applications from the European Space Agency [2], and utilized by the Digital Regulation Platform guidelines [3].

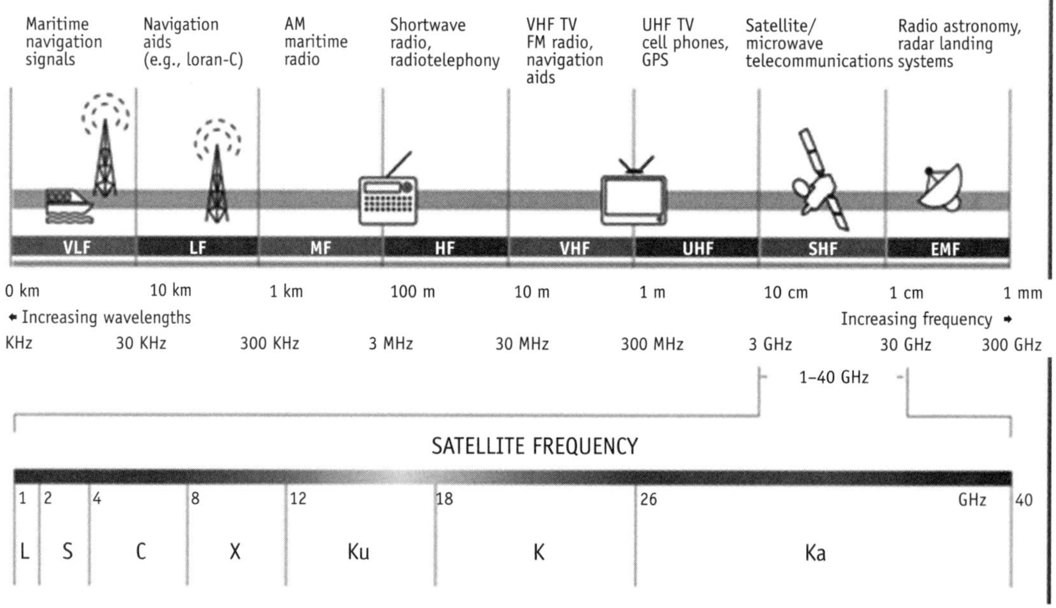

Figure 3.1
Radar and communications bands and their common applications. (From https://www.esa.int/ESA_Multimedia/Images/2013/11/Satellite_frequency_bands.)

3.2.1 RF Signal Collection from Ground

Many of the economically competitive countries have installed ground signal collection facilities for various reasons, such as communications, data transfer, and signaling. Some countries operate ground-based signal collection systems in collaboration with each other. For example, Russia and China operated ground-based signal collection systems in Cuba, Vietnam, and other countries. The Lourdes ground signals intelligence facility [4], located near Havana, Cuba, was one of the largest signals collection facilities operated by Russian foreign intelligence services. Currently, this facility is closed, the buildings were abandoned and reconstructed for new purpose. During the Cold War, Soviet intelligence officers, technicians, and engineers worked in this facility.

In 2000, it was reported that China signed an agreement with the Cuban government to share use of the facility for its own intelligence agency, though this information cannot be verified. In 2014, reports surfaced that Russia and Cuba had agreed to reopen the facility for use by Russian intelligence [5]. Other ground signal collections facilities in Cuba are Bejucal, Yaguajay, Santiago de Cuba, and Paseo. The Chinese government operated the Bejucal and Santiago de Cuba facilities. Initially, they tried to intercept the U.S. telephone communications and data traffic. Later, they tried to understand U.S. military satellite signals. The facility at Bejucal has ten satellite communication antennas that tried intercepting telephone communications in the U.S. This facility also ran a dedicated cyber warfare unit to focus on computer data traffic. The ground signal facility at Santiago de Cuba was established to collect U.S. military satellite communications signals.

Many European countries such as France, Germany, Italy, Spain, Norway, Sweden, and Finland have their own ground-based signal collection systems and facilities [1]. Countries in Asia, such as India, Japan, and South Korea, have designed ground based signals collection facilities for commercial and defensive purposes. It is important to appreciate the global operations of space-based and ground-based signals collections operations.

3.2.2 RF Signal Collection from Water

As the vast amount of Earth is covered with water (ocean, river, etc.), utilizing vessels for signal collection is common. In fact, ships of various sizes and submarines are used for signals collection for auxiliary general intelligence (AGI) [6]. Expensive vessels equipped with electronic instruments can collect signals over vast locations, offering a mobile platform, distributed coverage, and relay capabilities. Countries with large coastal borders often require signal collection capabilities to monitor activities.

China operates various spy ships for signal collections. These include the type 813 spy ship, type 814A spy ship, type 815 spy ship, and Yuan Wang–class tracking ship [7]. The Yuan Wang–class are used for tracking and support of satellite and intercontinental ballistic missiles by the People's Liberation Army Strategic Support Force of the People's Republic of China (PRC) [8]. It is important to note that the Yuan Wang–class is not a single class of identical design, but instead is a group of different designs grouped under the same series that share the one name.

According to news sources [9], Chinese People's Liberation Army-Navy (PLAN) commissioned its fifth improved Dongdiao-class (type 815A) electronic reconnaissance, or AGI ship. The ship will join China's North Sea Fleet. The PLAN has commissioned six Dongdiao-class vessels, five of the improved type 815A variety, and an older type 815 vessel. Between the one type 815 and the four type 815A, China's AGI fleet currently stands at five commissioned vessels. The PLAN's Tianwangxing was commissioned in December 2010 and entered service with their East Sea fleet. Three more vessels were commissioned in 2015, with two entering service with the South Sea fleet and one with the North Sea fleet. Chinese AGI ships drew attention for surveilling the Rim of the Pacific exercises in waters off Hawaii.

3.2.3 RF Signal Collection from Air

Along with ground and maritime systems, countries operate airborne systems for signal collections. Airborne systems can have an active transmitter to radiate the area of interest and process the received signals. It is also possible that the airborne system may have passive signal processing capability in that other signals of opportunity (TV signals, communication signals) can be used to identify objects of interest. China operated airborne signal intelligence platforms known as Y-8, a variant of the Russian An-12, for China's main electronic and reconnaissance aircraft [10, 11]. The Y-8 construction may be continuing for electronic warfare missions. The Shaanxi Y-8 or Yunshuji-8 aircraft is a medium-size medium-range transport aircraft produced by Shaanxi Aircraft Corporation in China, based on the Soviet Antonov An-12. It has become one of China's most popular military and civilian transport/cargo aircraft, with many variants produced and exported. Although the An-12 is no longer made, the Chinese Y-8 continues to be upgraded and produced. An estimated 169 Y-8 aircraft were built by 2010. In general, many of the industrialized nations operate aircraft enabled with RF signal collection systems to secure their air space from neighboring hostile nations or territories.

3.2.4 RF Signal Collection from Space

Space is the frontier for next generation science and technology development and exploration. A satellite can operate in synchronization with Earth's motion, or operate in a geostationary orbit observing a certain portion of the Earth. The satellite orbit can be circular, in which the center can be located at the center of the Earth, or elliptical, in which Earth's center can be located at one of the two foci of the ellipse. The satellite may orbit in equatorial planes (i.e., directly above the Earth's equator) or it may move to polar orbit (i.e., passing directly over both poles). It is also possible that a satellite may move in inclined orbits. Finally, a satellite may be operated from various altitudes commonly known as low-earth orbit (LEO) (50 to 2,000 km above the Earth), medium-earth orbit (MEO) (2,000 to 35,700 km), and high-earth orbit (HEO) (< 35,700 km). Future challenges for RF and optical laser surveillance, communication, and navigation result from the increased density of orbiting spacecraft, rocket bodies, fragmented debris, and discarded equipment.

Novel technology for space requires complex engineering design, as operating in space is quite different from Earth. For example, space electronics need to be radiation hardened, a requirement that requires extra cost and engineering considerations [12]. A single mistake on the overall spacecraft design can cause a multimillion dollar investment to be obsolete. Thus, space technology and possible points of failures are studied extensively to avoid unsuccessful outcomes. As a result, more nations are investing in space mission and technology development for national security. Though U.S. and Russia were the frontrunners of space technology development, gradually more nations are investing in outer space exploration [13]. Countries include European nations, such as France, Germany, Italy, and Finland. In addition, Asian countries, such as China and India, also have a huge focus on space technology. Figure 3.2 gives an example of notional interception of terrestrial signals from space.

Satellites enable signal collection from space, and historically, remote sensing is an application of spaceborne measurements. Though signals could be electro-optical, infrared, or radio frequency, processing these signals provides ground information for such vegetations, aftermath of a natural disaster, and pattern of life. Advanced nations are increasingly developing space technologies for civilian and military missions [14, 15].

China has become a contender for outer space exploration. Though China built its first rudimentary rockets in 900 A.D., China's space program began in the 1950s. The China National Space Administration (CNSA) was established in 1988. In 2003, China was the third country in the world to send a human into space and

Figure 3.2
Example of notional interception of terrestrial signals from space. (From 300px-Rhyolite_sat.svg.png (300×224) (wikimedia.org).)

safely return them to Earth, after the early successes of the United States and the former Soviet Union in the 1960s. The China Academy of Space Technology (CAST) and CNSA collaborate in developing space technologies.

China's first satellite, BeiDou-1, was an experimental regional navigation system. It was launched on October 31, 2000, as China began to build its own satellite navigation system. BeiDou-1 consisted of four satellites. The satellites themselves were based on the Chinese DFH-3 geostationary communications satellite. Unlike the American GPS, Russian GLONASS, and European Galileo systems, which use medium-earth orbit satellites, BeiDou-1 used satellites in geostationary orbit. The system does not require a large BeiDou-1 constellation of satellites. However, it limits the coverage to areas on Earth where the satellites are visible. BeiDou-1 was decommissioned at the end of 2012, after which the BeiDou-2 system became operational. In 2020, China launched the BeiDou-3 system (BDS-3) that includes three GEO satellites and twenty-four MEO satellites, which include signals of various frequencies.

3.3 Altitude and Shape of Orbits

From early days on, various altitudes and shapes of orbits have been studied and identified for cost-effective and strategic radio frequency signal collection and communications. Based on the altitude, low-earth orbit, medium-earth orbit, and high-earth orbit have been defined [16]. Other important orbits derived from these three main categories include geostationary orbit and Molniya orbit. Table 3.1 presents the various orbits and their altitudes (from Earth's surface). Figure 3.3 shows various orbits based on altitudes from Earth and space.

Table 3.1
Various Orbits and Their Altitudes from Earth's Surface

Orbits	Altitude	Orbital Period
Low-earth orbit (LEO)	160 to 2,000 km	1.5 to 2.0 hours
Medium-earth orbit (MEO)	2,000 to 35,780 km	2 to 24 hours
High-earth orbit (HEO)	~36,000 km	>24 hours

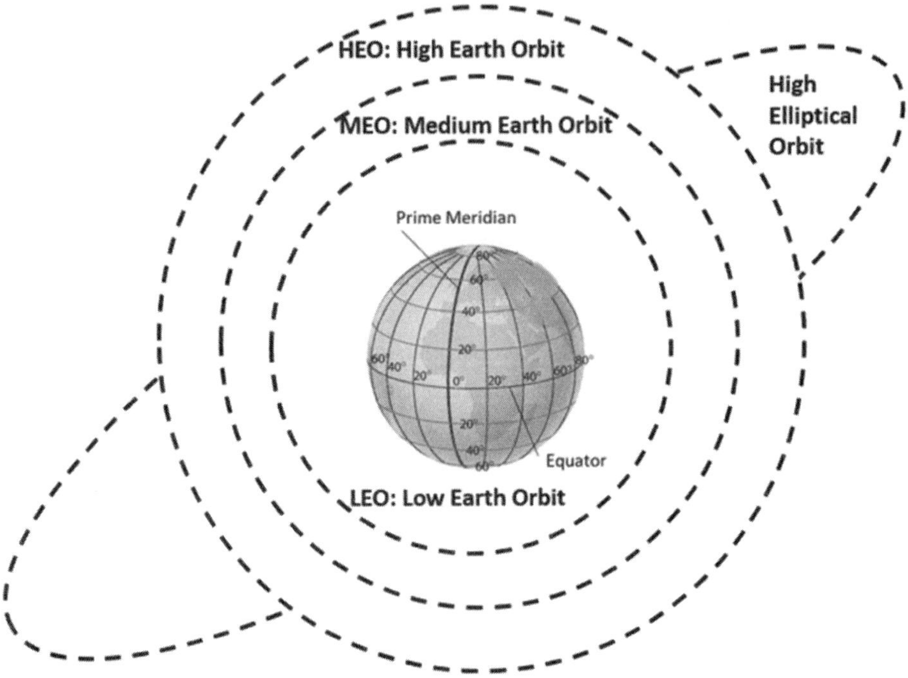

Figure 3.3
Various orbits based on altitudes from Earth and space.

3.3.1 Low-Earth Orbit

The low-earth orbit is the closest orbit to the Earth's surface. The altitude for LEO ranges approximately from 160 km to 2,000 km. In general, most commercial aircraft fly at an altitude of approximately 14 km. Even the lowest LEO is more than ten times higher than that. For a geosynchronous orbit, it must orbit along Earth's equator; however, LEO satellites do not always have to follow a particular path around Earth in the same way so there are more available paths for satellites in LEO. This makes LEO a commonly used orbit.

LEO is commonly used for satellite imaging/remote sensing. Since this orbit is close to the Earth, it captures a higher resolution imagery. The International Space Station (ISS) is in this orbit (400 km at LEO). Satellites in this orbit travel at a speed of around 7.8 km/sec; thus, a satellite takes approximately 90 minutes to circle Earth. The ISS can travel around Earth about 16 times a day.

One of the disadvantages of LEO is that individual LEO satellites are less useful for tasks such as telecommunication because they move so fast across the sky, and therefore require a lot of effort to track from ground stations. To mitigate this issue, communications satellites in LEO often work as part of a large constellation. In this case, multiple satellites provide constant coverage of an area of interest and can work together as a network to provide constant and wide-area coverage of the Earth.

Some of the important satellites in LEO include the International Space Station (400 km), Iridium telecom satellite (780 km), various Earth observation satellites (ESO) including Envisat, Landsat, Moderate Resolution Imaging Spectroradiometer (MODIS), Sentinel, GeoEye, and WorldView, as well as the Hubble Space Telescope (540 km) and Chinese Tiangong.

3.3.2 Medium-Earth Orbit

Medium-earth orbit is situated above the LEO orbit, as depicted in Figure 3.4. The altitude for MEO ranges from approximately 2,000

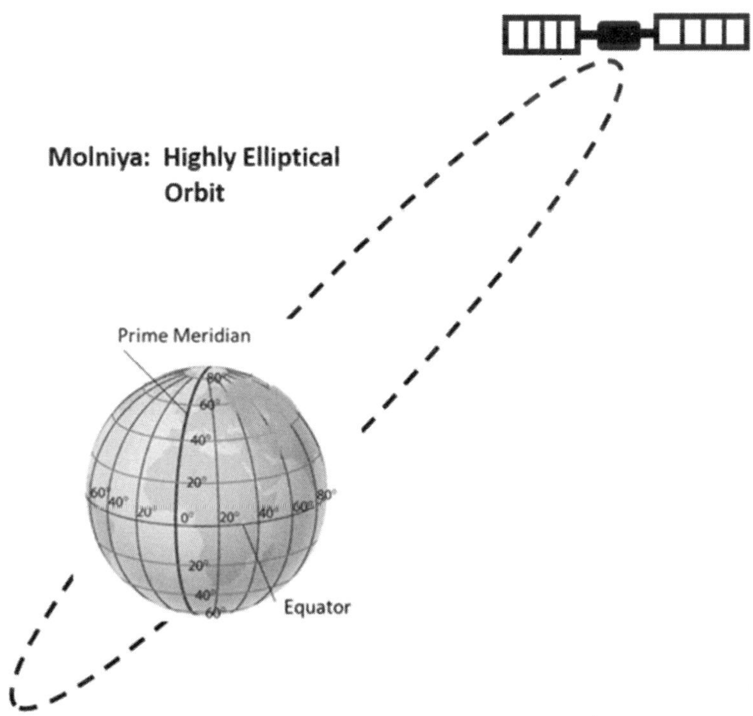

Figure 3.4
Notional diagram for the Molniya orbit.

km to 35,780 km above the Earth. Several navigational satellites are located at MEO. These are the American Global Positioning System (GPS), Russian GLONASS, European Galileo, and Chinese BeiDou navigation satellite system. Several telecommunications satellites, such as European O3b and American Telstar, are also located in MEO. Two of the most important MEO are semisynchronous orbit and Molniya orbit.

3.3.2.1 Semisynchronous Orbit

The semisynchronous orbit is almost a circular orbit with low eccentricity located at approximately 20,200 km above the surface. A satellite takes approximately 12 hours to complete an orbit at this altitude. In 24 hours, the satellite can cross the same point twice. This orbit is important as it is consistent and highly predictable. As mentioned, GPS satellites use this semisynchronous MEO.

3.3.2.2 Molniya Orbit

A special MEO, the Molniya orbit, was invented by Russian scientists for observing high latitudes, in particular at the North Pole. The Molniya orbit has a high eccentricity (0.722) and inclination (63.4 degrees). A geostationary orbit is important for the constant view it provides of the Earth's surface. However, at a geostationary location, a satellite is stationed at the equator, so this strategy does not work well for observing extreme northern or southern locations. The Molniya orbit addresses this shortcoming of the geostationary orbit. One of the characteristics of the Molniya orbit is that it has high eccentricity, as shown in Figure 3.4. One focus is close to Earth and the other one extremely far away. Due to Earth's gravity, a satellite moves rapidly when it is close to Earth and slows down as it moves away. Hence, a satellite spends more time at the top of its orbit farthest from the Earth. A satellite in a Molniya orbit takes 12 hours to complete the rotation; however, it spends about two-thirds of that time over one hemisphere (northern edge). Similar to the semisynchronous orbit, a satellite in the Molniya orbit passes over the same path every 24 hours. This type of orbit is useful for communications in the far north or south.

3.3.3 High-Earth Orbit

High-earth orbit is located above the MEO at an altitude of approximately 36,000 km. The orbital periods at HEO are more than 24 hours. Some of the important satellites at HEO include NASA's IBEX (Interstellar Boundary Explorer) and TESS (Transiting Exoplanet Survey Satellite) that study the solar system.

3.3.4 Special Orbit Terminology

There are special terms for some orbits. *Geosynchronous orbits* are circular orbits around the Earth that have a period of 24 hours. A geosynchronous orbit with an inclination of zero degrees is called a *geostationary orbit*, as shown in Figure 3.5. In a geostationary orbit, a spacecraft stays constant at the Earth's equator, making it ideal for some types of communication and meteorological satellites. To reach geosynchronous orbit, a spacecraft is first launched into an

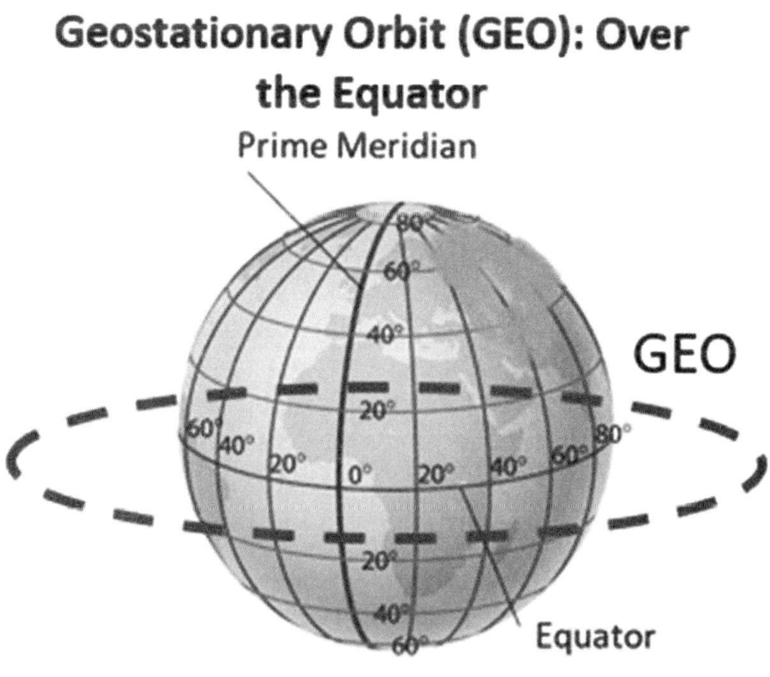

Figure 3.5
Geostationary orbit over the equator.

elliptical orbit with an apogee of 35,786 km called a *geosynchronous transfer orbit (GTO)*. The orbit is then circularized by propelling the spacecraft's engine at apogee.

Polar orbits (PO) are orbits with an inclination of 90 degrees. Polar orbits are useful for satellites that carry out mapping and/or surveillance operations because as the planet rotates, the spacecraft has access to virtually every point on the planet's surface. A *sun-synchronous orbit (SSO)* is a special type of polar orbit. Satellites in SSO, traveling over the polar regions, are synchronous with the Sun. As result, the satellite always visits the same spot at the same local time. As an example, at SSO, a satellite passes a city at the exact time during each orbit. A sun-synchronous orbit is useful for imaging, reconnaissance, and weather satellites.

3.4 Orbital Mechanics

Understanding orbital mechanics is important in designing signals collection from space, and interaction with ground/surface electronics. Johannes Keppler (in 1600) discovered that when a planet orbits, it forms an ellipse. When space satellites orbit Earth, they form an ellipse (i.e., their fly-by path forms an ellipse). Orbits are described by six parameters, or elements, known as Keplerian elements. Two of these parameters describe the size and shape, two describe orientation, and the remaining two describe the position of the orbit. Size and shape are represented by semimajor axis (a) and eccentricity (e), orientations are known as inclination (i) and ascending node (Ω), and positions are argument of periapsis (ω) and true anomaly (ν).

The following review of an ellipse clarifies the parameters that control an orbit. Figure 3.6 presents the geometry of an ellipse. The center of the ellipse is C, F1 and F2 are two foci, and c is the length from center of the ellipse to the focus F1 or F2. The distance of the major axis is $2a$ and semimajor axis is a; similarly, the distance of minor axis is $2b$ and semiminor axis is b. Mathematically, the equation of the ellipse is:

$$\frac{x^2}{a^2} + \frac{y^2}{b^2} = 1 \tag{3.1}$$

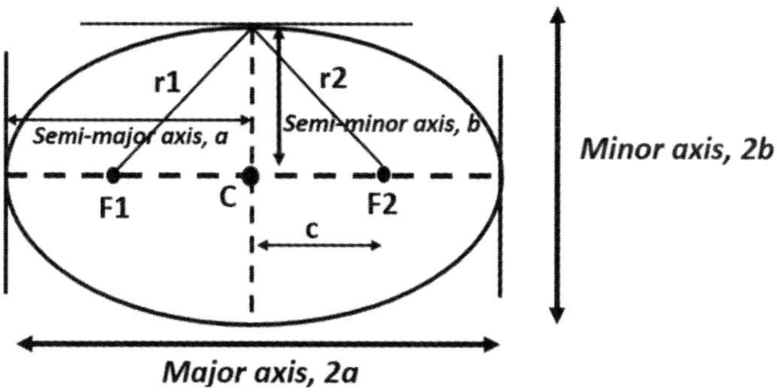

Figure 3.6
Geometry of an ellipse.

The eccentricity of an ellipse is defined as:

$$e = \frac{c}{a} = \sqrt{1 - \frac{b^2}{a^2}} \tag{3.2}$$

The eccentricity of the ellipse describes how narrow or wide the ellipse is.

Figure 3.7 presents six orbital elements needed to mathematically describe an orbit. We assume that the path of a satellite forms an elliptical shape with Earth or a point is located/situated on one of the two foci. This point is also known as a primary. Periapsis (i.e., *perigee* for Earth) is the point in the elliptical orbit that is closest to the primary. Apoapsis (i.e., *apogee* for Earth) is the farthest point to the primary. Inclination angle or the tilt (i) is the angle between the orbital plane and the equatorial plane. When a satellite moves/crosses the equatorial plane from south to north, the node is called *ascending node*. When a satellite moves/crosses the equatorial plane from north to south, the node is called *descending node*. The *longitude of the ascending node* (or swivel) is the angle between the vernal equinox and ascending node. The *argument of periapsis* is the angular distance between the ascending node and the point of periapsis/perigee. The time of periapsis passage is the time it takes for a satellite to move through its point of periapsis.

We will introduce a few more definitions here, prograde, retrograde, and sidereal period. In our solar system, *prograde* rotation

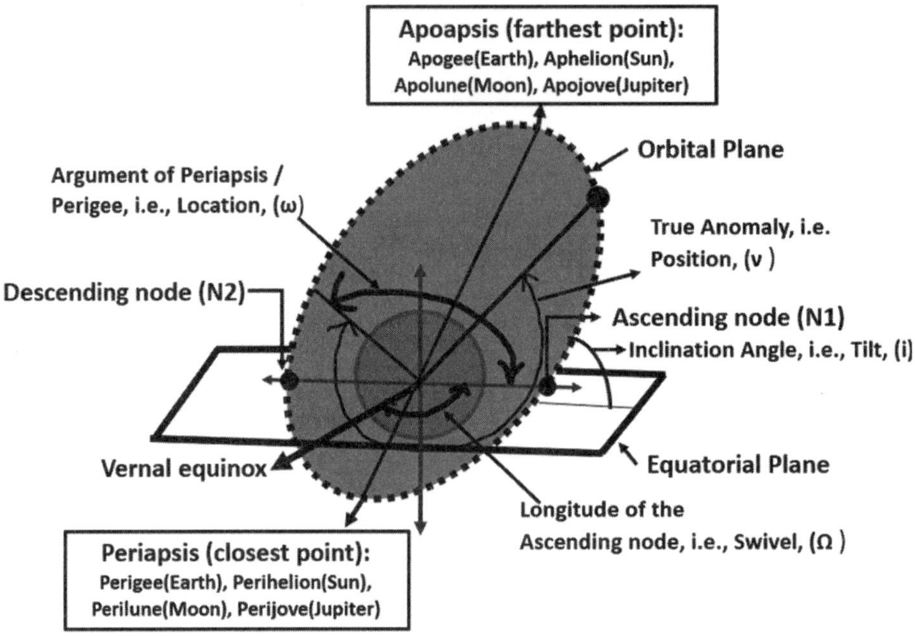

Figure 3.7
Elliptical orbit and terminology.

means the direction of rotation same as that of the Sun. It is in the counterclockwise direction when viewed from the North Pole. *Retrograde* rotation means the direction of rotation in opposite to that of the Sun, so in a clockwise rotation. For satellites, the reference object is our planet instead of the Sun. It was observed that all planets in the solar system, except Venus and Uranus, have prograde rotation. The *sidereal orbital period* is the orbital period, determined by a 360 degree revolution of one celestial body around another. For example, the Earth orbiting the Sun, relative to the fixed stars in the sky.

3.5 Conclusion

RF signals collection is found in various locations such as ground, water, air, and space. An important component of the future of signals collection is from space, so we have provided an overview of orbital mechanics, including terminology necessary for understanding a space system and the locations of space equipment for geometrical and signals strength. A signal collection system from space involves developing the satellite system and locating it to a desired place in space (LEO, MEO, GEO, etc.). Future signals analysis experts must understand the communications and equipment for effective assessment and response.

References

[1] Signals Intelligence Operational Platforms by Nation, Wikipedia, https://en.wikipedia.org/wiki/Signals_intelligence_operational_platforms_by_nation.

[2] European Space Agency, "Satellite Frequency Bands," 2013, https://www.esa.int/ESA_Multimedia/Images/2013/11/Satellite_frequency_bands.

[3] "Overview of National Spectrum Licensing," The World Bank Digital Regulation Platform, June 10, 2020.

[4] Lourdes SIGINT Station, Wikipedia, https://en.wikipedia.org/wiki/Lourdes_SIGINT_station.

[5] GlobalSecurity, Lourdes Signals Intelligence Facility, https://www.globalsecurity.org/intell/world/cuba/lourdes.htm.

[6] "Understanding Soviet Naval Developments," Office of the Chief of Naval Operations, Department of the Navy, 1985.

[7] https://en.wikipedia.org/wiki/Spy_ship.

[8] Yuan Wang-Class Tracking Ship, https://en.wikipedia.org/wiki/Yuan_Wang-class_tracking_ship.

[9] Panda, A., "Chinese Navy Commissions Fifth Improved *Dongdiao*-Class Spy Ship," *The Diplomat*, January 13, 2017, https://thediplomat.com/2017/01/chinese-navy-commissions-fifth-improved-dongdiao-class-spy-ship/.

[10] Shaanxi Y-8, https://en.wikipedia.org/wiki/Shaanxi_Y-8.

[11] "Global Security, Y-8 Electronic Variants," https://www.globalsecurity.org/military/world/china/y-8-high-new.htm,

[12] Wertz, J. R., Everett, D. F., and Puschell, J. J., "Space Mission Engineering," *The New SMAD*, Hawthorne, CA: Microcosm Press, 2011.

[13] Petersen, C. C., *Space Exploration: Past, Present, Future*, Gloucestershire, UK: Amberley Books, 2017.

[14] Branigan, T., and Sample, I., "China Unveils Rival to International Space Station," *The Guardian*, April 26, 2011, www.theguardian.com/world/2011/apr/26/china-space-station-tiangong.

[15] Woerner, J., "Moon Village," *European Space Agency*, 2016, www.esa.int/About_Us/Ministerial_Council_2016/Moon_Village.

[16] *Catalog of Earth Satellite Orbits*, NASA Earth Observatory, https://earthobservatory.nasa.gov/features/OrbitsCatalog.

4

Radar Fundamentals

4.1 Introduction

This chapter reviews the basic concepts of radar in uncooperative signals collection and exploitation. The first part gives the fundamentals of radar and communications waveforms via Maxwell's equations. Then, the theory of electromagnetic (EM) waveform generation and absorption is considered per antennas, including transmission and reception of signals beam patterns and math details of radar beamwidth. Finally, the Friis radar equation is derived, and its impact upon the data link equation in the transmission/reception of signals.

4.2 Electromagnetic Theory

4.2.1 Maxwell's Equations

The transmission, propagation, and reception of radar and communications waveforms is governed by the mechanics of Maxwell's equations. These equations dictate the physical laws of EM field quantities as a function of the 3-D of space $\mathbf{r} = \{x, y, z\}$ and time t. The quantities are the electric field $\boldsymbol{E}(\mathbf{r}, t)$ and the magnetic field

$\boldsymbol{H}(\mathbf{r}, t)$, as shown in Figure 4.1. In addition, the electric displacement $\boldsymbol{D}(\mathbf{r}, t)$ and the magnetic flux density $\boldsymbol{B}(\mathbf{r}, t)$ are two other fields appearing in Maxwell's equations, derived from $\boldsymbol{E}(\mathbf{r}, t)$ and $\boldsymbol{H}(\mathbf{r}, t)$, respectively. The two source quantities are volumetric electric charge density $\rho(\mathbf{r}, t)$, and the volumetric electric current density $\boldsymbol{J}(\mathbf{r}, t)$. Figure 4.1 presents an example of a transverse EM wave of wavelength λ where the electric field $\boldsymbol{E}(\mathbf{r}, t)$, and the magnetic flux density $\boldsymbol{B}(\mathbf{r}, t)$, are both perpendicular to each other and to the direction of propagation.

James Clerk Maxwell originally derived the final form of the equations which bear his name through an understanding of the relationships between the fundamental EM quantities and those pertaining to vorticity in fluid dynamics. The equations in his derivation are lengthier than the modern compact formulation that is expressed in terms of the divergence (e.g., $\nabla \cdot \boldsymbol{E}(\mathbf{r}, t)$) and curl (e.g., $\nabla \times \boldsymbol{E}(\mathbf{r}, t)$) operators taught to students today. The curl is a vector operator describing a vector-field infinitesimal calculation of the 3-D $\{x, y, z\}$ Euclidean space, from which the vector length describes the magnitude, and the direction is the axis of maximum circulation (i.e., curl). The divergence is a vector operator describing vector-field scalar calculation of the volume density of the outward flux of the vector field from an infinitesimal volume around a point.

The first of the four Maxwell equations, in differential form, is given by *Faraday's law* [1]:

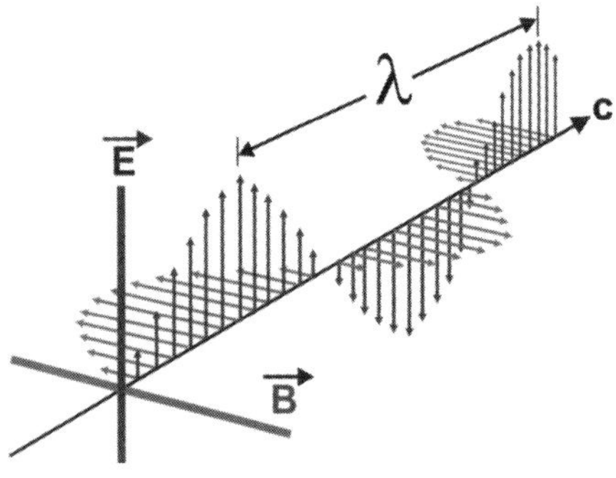

Figure 4.1

Maxwell's equations describe signal propagation, as with a transverse EM wave with wavelength λ. (Free license: Electromagnetic waves wavelength. Free vector graphic on Pixabay.)

$$\nabla \times \boldsymbol{E}(\mathbf{r},t) = -\frac{\partial \boldsymbol{B}(\mathbf{r},t)}{\partial t} \tag{4.1}$$

which relates the curl of electric field $\boldsymbol{E}(\mathbf{r}, t)$ to the time derivative of the magnetic flux density $\boldsymbol{B}(\mathbf{r}, t)$. The second equation is *Ampere's law*:

$$\nabla \times \boldsymbol{H}(\mathbf{r},t) = \frac{\partial \boldsymbol{D}(\mathbf{r},t)}{\partial t} + \boldsymbol{J}(\mathbf{r},t) \tag{4.2}$$

which expresses the curl of the magnetic field $\boldsymbol{H}(\mathbf{r}, t)$ to the electric current density $\boldsymbol{J}(\mathbf{r}, t)$ and the time derivative of the electric displacement $\boldsymbol{D}(\mathbf{r}, t)$. The third equation proves that there are no observed physical monopoles in nature, so that the corresponding divergence of the magnetic flux density $\boldsymbol{B}(\mathbf{r}, t)$ is zero:

$$\nabla \cdot \boldsymbol{B}(\mathbf{r},t) = 0 \tag{4.3}$$

The final Maxwell equation states that the divergence of the electric displacement $\boldsymbol{D}(\mathbf{r}, t)$, gives the electric charge density $\rho(\mathbf{r}, t)$:

$$\nabla \cdot \boldsymbol{D}(\mathbf{r},t) = \rho(\mathbf{r},t) \tag{4.4}$$

Finally, the constitutive equations provide the relationships between $\boldsymbol{E}(\mathbf{r}, t)$ and $\boldsymbol{D}(\mathbf{r}, t)$, and between $\boldsymbol{H}(\mathbf{r}, t)$ and $\boldsymbol{B}(\mathbf{r}, t)$ in terms of the scalar electric permittivity $\varepsilon(\mathbf{r}, t)$, and the magnetic permeability $\mu(\mathbf{r}, t)$ via:

$$\boldsymbol{B}(\mathbf{r},t) = \mu(\mathbf{r},t)\boldsymbol{H}(\mathbf{r},t) \tag{4.5}$$

$$\boldsymbol{D}(\mathbf{r},t) = \varepsilon(\mathbf{r},t)\boldsymbol{E}(\mathbf{r},t) \tag{4.6}$$

Electric permittivity measures the polarizability of a dielectric that a material with low permittivity polarizes less in response to an applied electric field. A material with high permittivity stores more energy in the material. In relation, the magnetic permeability measures the response to a magnetic field from a material with low permeability, where the magnetic flux density within the field is reduced. A material with high permeability becomes magnetized in the direction of the external field. In general, the electric permittivity and the magnetic permeability can be tensor dyads, but the use of scalar functions of position and time will be assumed here.

4.2.2 EM Wave Propagation

It is convenient to use phasor notation for computing solutions of Maxwell's equations for the propagation of radar and communications waveforms. *Phasor notation* is the expression of the field quantities, which are general functions of space **r** and time t, in a form corresponding to a single Fourier harmonic. The benefit of the phasor notation is the harmonics of a sinusoidal waveform with a single complex number that has an amplitude, A, phase angle θ, and the imaginary unit $j = \sqrt{-1}$, as shown in Figure 4.2:

$Z = x + j\,y;$ Rectangular Form

$Z = A \angle \theta;$ Polar Form

$Z = A\,(\cos\theta + j\,\sin\theta) = \theta\,\exp\,(j\theta\,);$ Exponential Form

where $A(t) = A\,\cos(\omega t \pm \delta)$, which is a transformation in the time domain to the frequency domain with ω as the angular frequency, and δ a phase constant.

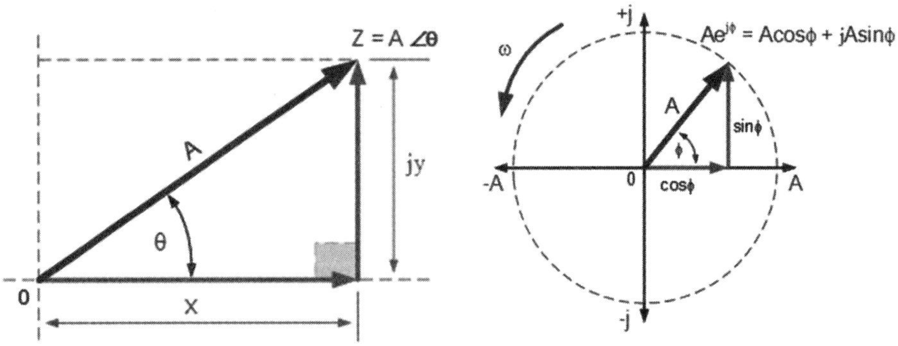

Figure 4.2
Graphical representation of a complex number, showing horizontal real axis and the vertical imaginary axis, as well as the magnitude A and phase θ.

For example, consider a single Fourier harmonic, characterized by the angular frequency ω, given by:

$$E(\mathbf{r},t) = \mathbf{E}_0(\mathbf{r})\cos(\omega t - \delta_0) \tag{4.7}$$

with $\mathbf{E}_0(\mathbf{r})$ a vector function of spatial position only and δ_0 equal to a phase constant.

The linearity of the Maxwell equation implies that the linear superposition of Fourier harmonics can apply. Thus, it is possible to consider just a single harmonic when seeking solutions, since general time dependence is possible by the superposition principle within the linear form of Maxwell's equations. Furthermore, the physical fields corresponding to the form of (4.7) involve computing the real part of the complex-valued quantities. That is, the desired phasor is a complex-valued quantity that can be expressed in the form:

$$E(\mathbf{r},t) = \mathrm{Re}\{\mathbf{E}_0(\mathbf{r})\exp(j\omega t)\} \tag{4.8}$$

Phasors can be used for the other time-dependent physical quantities of interest. For example, the magnetic field has the following form:

$$H(\mathbf{r},t) = \mathrm{Re}\{\mathbf{H}_0(\mathbf{r})\exp(j\omega t)\} \tag{4.9}$$

4.2.3 EM Wave Polarization

The polarization of EM waveforms is defined in terms of the vector direction of the electric field vector $E(\mathbf{r}, t)$ throughout its propagation within a medium of interest. For example, consider a waveform solution of Maxwell's equations where the surfaces of constant phase correspond to flat planes. For this case, the direction of propagation is in a direction that is normal to the planar surfaces of constant phase. For convenience, define a set of Cartesian coordinates $\mathbf{r} = \{x, y, z\}$ such that the $\{x, y\}$ coordinates correspond to the planar surfaces of constant phase and the z coordinate is defined so that waveform energy propagates in the $+z$ direction.

There exist various types of polarization used to describe a propagating waveform. The simplest type is *linear polarization*, as shown in Figure 4.3. For this case, the electric field vector $\boldsymbol{E}(\mathbf{r}, t)$ points in a single direction and does not change in time. The electric field phasor $\mathbf{E}_0(\mathbf{r})$ lies in a single direction and thus is real valued. Select the x coordinate so that the vector direction of the electric field phasor $\mathbf{E}_0(\mathbf{r})$ lies in the $+x$ direction:

$$\mathbf{E}_0(\mathbf{r}) = E_0 \exp(-jkz)\hat{\mathbf{x}} \tag{4.10}$$

with E_0 giving the scalar intensity of the electric field and the Cartesian unit vectors expressed in terms of the notation $\{\hat{\mathbf{x}}, \hat{\mathbf{y}}, \hat{\mathbf{z}}\}$. For this waveform, the magnetic field phasor $\mathbf{H}_0(\mathbf{r})$ lies in the $+y$ direction, completing the right-handed set of coordinates for this propagating plane wave.

Another type of polarization is *circular polarization*, which is used for satellite communications that pass through the ionosphere. In this case, the direction of the electric vector $\boldsymbol{E}(\mathbf{r}, t)$ rotates during the propagation of the waveform. Consider again a planar waveform that is propagating in the $+z$ direction, so that the $\boldsymbol{E}(\mathbf{r}, t)$ rotates within the plane defined by the $\{x, y\}$ coordinates. Then, electric field phasor $\mathbf{E}_0(\mathbf{r})$ for circular polarization has the form:

$$\mathbf{E}_0(\mathbf{r}) = E_0 \exp(-jkz)\{\hat{\mathbf{x}} \mp j\hat{\mathbf{y}}\} \tag{4.11}$$

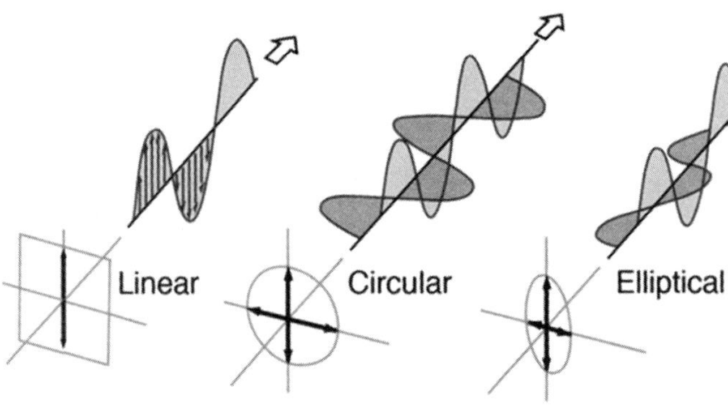

Figure 4.3
These figures present graphical representations of the electric field vector corresponding to three of the primary types of polarization: linear, circular, and elliptical [3].

in terms of the wavenumber k and the speed of light c. Thus, after a quarter of a period, the waveform polarization has rotated from the $\hat{\mathbf{x}}$ to the $\hat{\mathbf{y}}$ direction. The minus sign in (4.11) gives right-handed circular polarization, the plus sign corresponds to left-handed circular polarization.

Other polarizations that do not fit cleanly into linear or circular are typically referred to as having *elliptical polarization*. For these waveforms, the electric field vector $\mathbf{E}(\mathbf{r}, t)$ point traces the shape of an ellipse as the propagation proceeds for the duration of period. Then, the electric field phasor has the form:

$$\mathbf{E}_0(\mathbf{r}) = \left\{E_{x0}\hat{\mathbf{x}} \mp jE_{y0}\hat{\mathbf{y}}\right\}\exp(-jkz) \quad (4.12)$$

For elliptical polarization, the constant parameters E_{x0} and E_{y0} are real valued and unequal.

4.3 Antennas

In radio engineering, an antenna is the interface between radio waves propagating through space and electric currents moving in metal conductors, used with a transmitter or receiver [2]. In transmission, a radio transmitter supplies an electric current to the antenna's terminals, and the antenna radiates the energy from the current as electromagnetic waves (radio waves). In reception, an antenna intercepts some of the power of a radio wave to produce an electric current at its terminals, which in turn is applied to a receiver to be amplified. Antennas are essential components of all radio equipment.

An antenna is an array of conductors (elements), electrically connected to the receiver or transmitter. Antennas can be designed to transmit and receive radio waves in all horizontal directions equally (omnidirectional antennas), or preferentially in a particular direction (directional, high-gain, or beam antennas) (see Figure 4.4). An antenna may include components not connected to the transmitter, parabolic reflectors, horns, or parasitic elements, which serve to direct the radio waves into a beam or other radiation pattern.

The first antennas were built in 1888 by German physicist Heinrich Hertz in his pioneering experiments to prove the existence

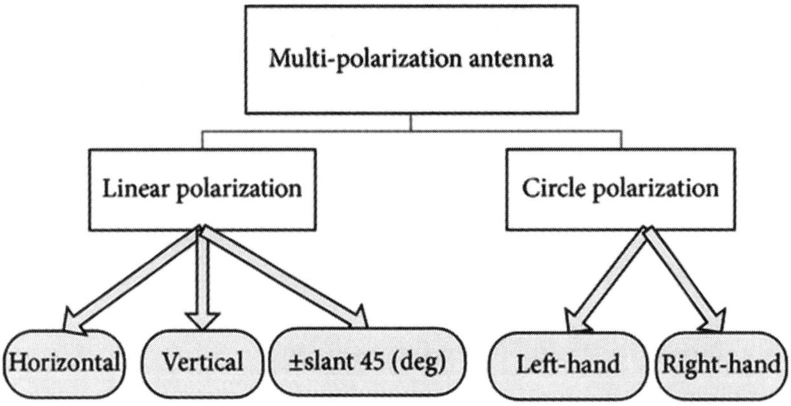

Figure 4.4
Multiple varieties of basic polarization are possible, with the primary categories given by linear and circular polarization.

of waves predicted by the electromagnetic theory of James Clerk Maxwell. Hertz placed dipole antennas at the focal point of parabolic reflectors for both transmitting and receiving [2]. Starting in 1895, Guglielmo Marconi began developing antennas practical for long distance, wireless telegraphy, for which he received a Nobel Prize [2].

4.3.1 Pure Magnetic Dipole Antenna Concept

Exact solutions of Maxwell's equations typically exist only for simple geometries. Complicated geometries often require approximate analytic solutions or detailed numerical modeling. One example of an exact solution of Maxwell's equations is based upon the modeling of infinite plane wave propagation using the equations above, where the wavefronts extend over all directions along infinite planes. The problem with this approach is that the electric currents which drive the EM plane waves also lie within infinite planes that are orthogonal to the direction of propagation. That is, this solution is unrealistic in being characterized by an unbounded source of electric current.

Recent work in [4, 5] has revealed the existence of an exact solution of Maxwell's equations for all space where the driving electric currents are confined within the surface of nonzero radius $r = a$.

This sphere antenna concept gives another solution to Maxwell's equations for all space, but with an electric current density within a bounded volume in all three dimensions (i.e., the current density does not extend to infinity in any direction). The spherical antenna concept is used to describe many basic antenna concepts within this section. The theoretical development presented next applies the basic concepts of spherical expansion functions, used in the calculation of the EM fields emanating from circular loop antennas [6–14].

The subject of pure magnetic dipole antenna begins with a particular form of electric current density that is confined within a theoretically infinitely thin shell of radius a. This electric current flows only in the azimuthal direction about an axis that is selected to be the $\hat{\mathbf{z}}$ for a set of Cartesian coordinates $\mathbf{r} = \{x, y, z\}$, with corresponding unit vectors $\{\hat{\mathbf{x}}, \hat{\mathbf{y}}, \hat{\mathbf{z}}\}$. The origin of the $\{x, y, z\}$ coordinates is the center of the sphere. For simplicity, assume a sinusoidal temporal dependence $\psi(t)$ of the electric current as a function of time t, although this current can have a more general time dependence as well. Another important assumption is that the current density is proportional to the sine function applied to the polar angle θ of the spherical coordinates $\mathbf{r} = \{r, \theta, \phi\}$, with corresponding unit vectors $\{\hat{\mathbf{r}}(\theta, \phi), \hat{\boldsymbol{\theta}}(\theta, \phi), \hat{\boldsymbol{\phi}}(\phi)\}$. Thus, the assumed azimuthal electric current flows only in the $\hat{\boldsymbol{\phi}}(\phi)$ direction. These assumptions yield the following form for the surface current density vector [4]:

$$\mathbf{K}(\mathbf{r},t) = \tilde{I}\sin(\theta)\hat{\boldsymbol{\phi}}(\phi)\psi(t) \tag{4.13}$$

In (4.13), the parameter $\tilde{I}$ is proportional to the integrated electric current that flows on the sphere's surface. The relationship between the Cartesian coordinates $\mathbf{r} = \{x, y, z\}$ and the spherical coordinates $\mathbf{r} = \{r, \theta, \phi\}$ is the following:

$$\begin{aligned} x &= r\sin(0)\cos(\phi), \\ y &= r\sin(\theta)\sin(\phi), \\ z &= r\cos(\theta). \end{aligned} \tag{4.14}$$

The assumed surface current density $\mathbf{K}(\mathbf{r}, t)$ of (4.13) can be expressed in a form that is conducive for manipulation within Maxwell's equation by using the Dirac delta function $\delta(x)$ defined via the integral:

$$\int_q^p f(x)\delta(x-b)\,dx = \begin{cases} f(b), & \text{for } q < b < p \\ 0, & \text{otherwise} \end{cases} \tag{4.15}$$

Then, the volumetric electric current density vector $\mathbf{J}(\mathbf{r}, t)$ that appears within Maxwell's equations follows from the assumed form of $\mathbf{K}(\mathbf{r}, t)$ of (4.13) [4]:

$$\mathbf{J}(r,t) = \frac{I_0}{2}\frac{\delta(r-a)}{r}\sin(\theta)\hat{\boldsymbol{\phi}}(\phi)\psi(t) \tag{4.16}$$

In (4.16), the parameter constant I_0 corresponds to the total electric current that flows on the surface of the sphere, as revealed in [4]. The electric current at any given instant in time t is given by $I_0\psi(t)$.

The linearity of Maxwell's equations implies that it is possible and convenient to calculate solutions for a single Fourier harmonic, so that the summation of many such harmonics can be used to generate more general solutions based upon more complicated electric currents. Thus, consider a given single Fourier harmonic that is characterized by an angular temporal frequency ω. The corresponding wavelength λ and the wavenumber k are determined by the magnetic permeability μ and the electric permittivity ε of the intervening medium via:

$$k = \frac{2\pi}{\lambda} = \omega\sqrt{\varepsilon\mu} \tag{4.17}$$

Then, examine the EM fields resulting from a single Fourier harmonic of the electric current density, which can be expressed as [4]:

$$\mathbf{J}(\mathbf{r}',t) = \mathbf{J}(\mathbf{r}')\exp(i\omega t) \tag{4.18}$$

$$\mathbf{J}(\mathbf{r}') = J_\phi(r',\theta')\hat{\boldsymbol{\phi}}(\phi') \tag{4.19}$$

$$J_\phi(r',\theta') = \frac{I_0}{2}\frac{\delta(r'-a)}{r'}\sin(\theta') \tag{4.20}$$

These equations comply with the convention that source points are denoted with primed coordinates and observation points utility with unprimed coordinates. Also, in (4.18), the symbol $i \equiv \sqrt{-1}$ denotes the imaginary unit.

The EM fields are calculated by using the radiation integrals to calculate the vector potential **A**(**r**′, *t*) based upon the prescribed spherically shaped electric current density of (4.18) to (4.20) via:

$$\mathbf{A}(r) \equiv \frac{\mu}{4\pi}\int d^3r' \frac{\mathbf{J}(\mathbf{r}')\exp(-ikR(\mathbf{r},\mathbf{r}'))}{R(\mathbf{r},\mathbf{r}')} \tag{4.21}$$

Here, d^3r' denotes the volumetric integration element, and $R(\mathbf{r}, \mathbf{r}')$ gives the distance between a given electric current point **r**′ and a selected spatial point **r** of observation:

$$R(\mathbf{r},\mathbf{r}') \equiv |\mathbf{r} - \mathbf{r}'| = \sqrt{\{x - x'\}^2 + \{y - y'\}^2 + \{z - z'\}^2} \tag{4.22}$$

Use of the electric current density **J**(**r**′, *t*) in (4.18) to (4.20) implies that the vector potential of (4.21) can be expressed in the form [4]:

$$\mathbf{A}(\mathbf{r},t) = \mathbf{A}(\mathbf{r})\exp(i\omega t) \tag{4.23}$$

$$\mathbf{A}(\mathbf{r}) = A_\phi(r,\theta)\hat{\boldsymbol{\phi}}(\phi) \tag{4.24}$$

$$A_\phi(r,\theta) \equiv -\frac{i\mu I_0 ka}{2} f_1(kr)\sin(\theta) \tag{4.25}$$

In (4.25), the function is defined via:

$$f_1(kr) = \begin{cases} h_1^{(2)}(ka)j_1(kr), & \text{for } r < a \\ j_1(ka)h_1^{(2)}(kr), & \text{for } r > a \end{cases} \tag{4.26}$$

Here, $j_1(kr)$ and $h_1^{(2)}(ka)$ denote two spherical Bessel functions of order unity, being of the first and third kinds, respectively.

The vector potential **A**(**r**, *t*) in (4.23) to (4.26) is defined for all space **r**, both interior $r < a$ to the current density sphere and exterior

$r > a$ to it. Thus, it is possible to compute the corresponding electric field **E**(**r**, t) and magnetic field **H**(**r**, t) for all space as well. The vector potential **A**(**r**, t) of (4.23) to (4.26) has zero divergence. Therefore, the electric field is computed via:

$$\mathbf{E}(\mathbf{r},t) \equiv -\frac{\partial \mathbf{A}(\mathbf{r},t)}{\partial t} \tag{4.27}$$

Reference [4] reveals that the electric field **E**(**r**, t) can be expressed in terms of spherical Bessel functions as well via [4]:

$$\mathbf{E}(\mathbf{r},t) = \mathbf{E}(\mathbf{r})\exp(i\omega t) \tag{4.28}$$

$$\mathbf{E}(\mathbf{r}) = E_\phi(r,\theta)\hat{\boldsymbol{\phi}}(\phi) \tag{4.29}$$

$$E_\phi(r,\theta) \equiv -\frac{\omega\mu I_0 ka}{2} f_1(kr)\sin(\theta) \tag{4.30}$$

The electric field **E**(**r**, t) in (4.28) to (4.30) reveals that the only nonzero vector component lies in the azimuthal $\hat{\boldsymbol{\phi}}$ (ϕ) direction.

Likewise, the magnetic field **H**(**r**, t) also can be calculated for all space **r** by using:

$$\mathbf{H}(\mathbf{r},t) \equiv \frac{1}{\mu}\nabla \times \mathbf{A}(\mathbf{r},t) \tag{4.31}$$

Reference [4] shows that the magnetic field **H**(**r**, t) has components that are nonzero in the spherical radial and polar directions, and these components also utilize spherical Bessel functions [4]:

$$\mathbf{H}(\mathbf{r},t) = \mathbf{H}(\mathbf{r})\exp(i\omega t) \tag{4.32}$$

$$\mathbf{H}(\mathbf{r}) = H_r(r,\theta)\hat{\mathbf{r}}(\theta,\phi) + H_\theta(r,\theta)\hat{\boldsymbol{\phi}}(\theta,\phi) \tag{4.33}$$

$$H_r(r,\theta) = -\frac{iI_0 ka}{2}\cos(\theta)\frac{2}{r}f_1(kr) \tag{4.34}$$

$$H_\theta(r,\theta) = \frac{iI_0 ka}{2}\sin(\theta)\left\{kg_0(kr) - \frac{1}{r}f_1(kr)\right\} \tag{4.35}$$

The following definition involving spherical Bessel functions is used in (4.35):

$$g_0(kr) \equiv \begin{cases} h_1^{(2)}(ka)j_0(kr), & \text{for } r < a \\ j_1(ka)h_0^{(2)}(kr), & \text{for } r > a \end{cases} \tag{4.36}$$

Here, $j_n(kr)$ and $h_n^{(2)}(ka)$ denote two spherical Bessel functions of order n, again of the first and third kinds, respectively, as in (4.26),

The electric field $\mathbf{E}(\mathbf{r}, t)$ of (4.26), and (4.28) to (4.30), and the magnetic field $\mathbf{H}(\mathbf{r}, t)$ of (4.26), and (4.32) to (4.36) are both defined for all space $\mathbf{r}$. Reference [4] reveals that $\mathbf{E}(\mathbf{r}, t)$ and $\mathbf{H}(\mathbf{r}, t)$ satisfy Maxwell's equations (4.1) to (4.4) for all space as well. Thus, this magnetic sphere dipole antenna design yields an exact Maxwell solution for a electric current density $\mathbf{J}(\mathbf{r}', t)$ that is bounded within the finite region of a sphere surface.

4.3.2 Transmission and Reception Beam Patterns

A useful quantity to calculate based upon the electric field $\mathbf{E}(\mathbf{r}, t)$ and the magnetic field $\mathbf{H}(\mathbf{r}, t)$ is the complex-valued Poynting vector $\mathbf{W}(\mathbf{r}, t)$ [2]:

$$\mathbf{W}(\mathbf{r},t) \equiv \frac{1}{2}\mathbf{E}(\mathbf{r},t) \times \mathbf{H}^*(\mathbf{r},t) \tag{4.37}$$

Here, the superscript * corresponds to the complex conjugate. For the subject spherical electric current density, the Poynting vector has radial $\hat{\mathbf{r}}(\theta, \phi)$ and spherical polar $\hat{\boldsymbol{\theta}}(\theta, \phi)$ components [4]:

$$\mathbf{W}(\mathbf{r},t) = -\frac{1}{2}\left\{E_\phi(r,t)H_\theta^*(r,t)\hat{\mathbf{r}}(\theta,\phi) - E_\phi(r,t)H_r^*(r,t)\hat{\boldsymbol{\theta}}(\theta,\phi)\right\} \tag{4.38}$$

The radial component of the Poynting vector gives the outward power flow emanating from the antenna. It is found in [4] that this outward radial power flow can be expressed as:

$$W_r(r,\theta) = \frac{i\eta I_0^2 k^4 a^2}{8}\sin^2(\theta) w_r(kr) \tag{4.39}$$

$$w_r(kr) \equiv f_1(kr)\left\{g_0^*(kr) - \frac{1}{kr} f_1^*(kr)\right\} \tag{4.40}$$

Equation (4.39) reveals that the power of the radiation pattern scales as $\sin^2(\theta)$ in the spherical polar direction. In addition, this power pattern is invariant with regards to the azimuthal angle ϕ. The power of the radiation pattern of the electric dipole antenna also scales as $\sin^2(\theta)$ and is invariant with regards to ϕ. However, the roles of the magnetic and electric fields are reversed for the electric dipole antenna, the magnetic field $\mathbf{H}(\mathbf{r}, t)$ lies only in the azimuthal direction $\hat{\boldsymbol{\phi}}(\theta, \phi)$, and the electric field $\mathbf{E}(\mathbf{r}, t)$ has components in both the radial $\hat{\mathbf{r}}(\theta, \phi)$ and spherical polar $\hat{\boldsymbol{\theta}}(\theta, \phi)$ components.

The geometric gain G is equal to the ratio of the Poynting vector power at a given angle relative to that of the equivalent isotropic antenna. For the case of a $\sin^2(\theta)$ power pattern, as applies to both the spherical magnetic dipole design and the linear electric dipole, the geometric gain has a value of 3/2. Both of these dipole antenna designs give a relatively small gain as a singleton, so that EM radiation flows equally in all azimuthal directions.

In many cases, it is helpful to use dipoles as elements within a radar array, which can provide an electronic steering capability in both transmission and reception. Such use of an overall array design often enables significantly higher values of the gain [15]. That is, the ability to transmit and/or receive EM energy in a particular direction is enhanced. For example, Figures 4.5 and 4.6 present an example of a relatively sharp and narrow radar beam, where most of the radar energy is directed along this way. Very little energy flows in other directions, although there can exist both sidelobes and a backlobe for the overall antenna design.

There is significant freedom available in the design and operation of a radar system. A given system can support the transmission and reception of various radiation patterns of the radar power. These transmission beams can be omnidirectional azimuthally, and useful for communications applications, or significantly directional with various beam shapes and gains. A taxonomy graphic presenting the various degrees of freedom available to the radar designer in shown in Figure 4.7.

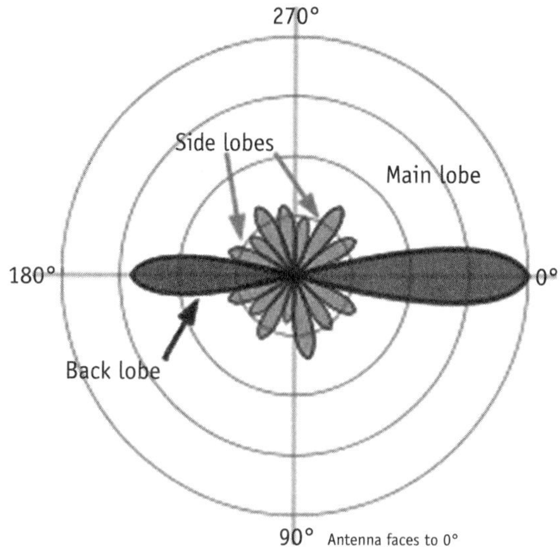

Figure 4.5
A 2-D representation of the gain pattern corresponding to an antenna, revealing the mainlobe, a backlobe, and various sidelobes [16].

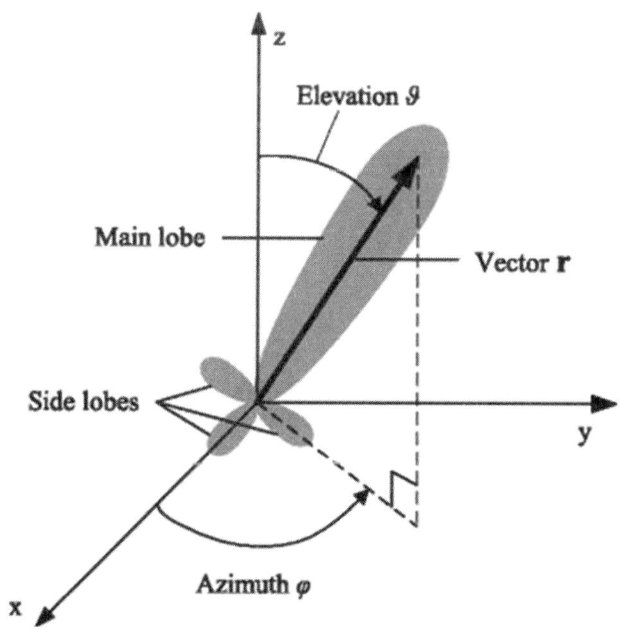

Figure 4.6
A 3-D representation of the gain pattern corresponding to an antenna, revealing the mainlobe, a backlobe, and various sidelobes [16].

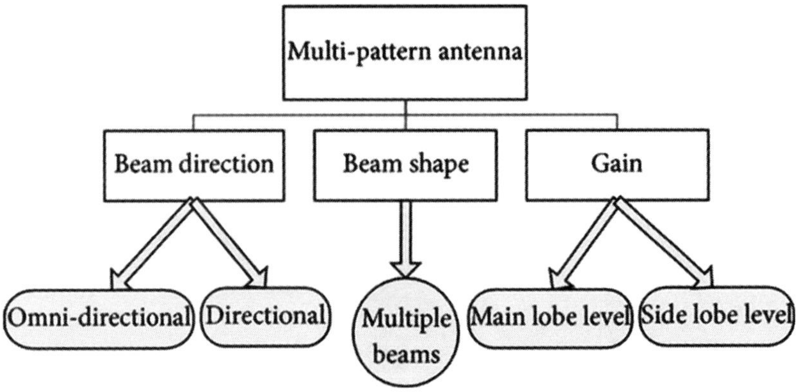

Figure 4.7
Taxonomy graphic presenting the various degrees of freedom available to the radar designer [17].

4.4 Radar Equation

4.4.1 Signal Power Over One-Way Link

An understanding of the transmission and reception of radar waveform requires a detailed examination of the radar range equations [15]. The radar range equation provides a quantitative method for calculating the radar energy at the front end of a radar antenna receiver based upon the power that is injected into the antenna at the radar transmitter. This one-way link equation also provides the foundation of the derivation of the radar range equation, which quantifies the expected received signal power due to the echo of the transmitted radar waveform off of a target within the interrogated scene of the radar system.

The analysis begins with the power of P_t of the radar transmission antenna. The transmission antenna is also characterized by an angle-dependent power gain pattern $G_t(\theta, \phi)$, in terms of a spherical azimuthal angle ϕ and a spherical elevation angle θ. For electric dipole antennas and the magnetic dipole concept describe above, this gain pattern scales as the square of the sine of the spherical elevation angle θ (i.e., $\sin^2(\theta)$), as developed in (4.39). The use of other antenna designs and that of arrays of simple elements permits high gains to be achieved. We will use the notation G_t to describe the value of angle-dependent gain pattern $G_t(\theta, \phi)$ in a particular direction of interest characterized by a spherical azimuthal angle ϕ_t

$= \phi_{t0}$, and a spherical elevation angle $\theta_t = \theta_{t0}$ relative to that of the transmission antenna. The product P_tG_t is also called the effective radiative power of the antenna.

As the radar waveform spreads out into the surrounding environment, its power falls off as the surface area of a sphere (i.e., $4\pi R^2$), with R equal to the distance from the transmission antenna phase center to a spatial point of interest in the surrounding environment. Thus, the incident signal power density W_i arriving at a particular location is given by:

$$W_i = \frac{P_t G_t}{4\pi R^2} \tag{4.41}$$

For a one-way radar link, this receiver power enters the receiver antenna that is separated by a distance of R from the transmission antenna. For communications applications, this receiver power provides the desired signal information that is to be demodulated to extract the needed information. The signal power competes with the ambient noise and interference power that enters the receiver antenna, as well as that of the internal thermal noise power generated by the receiver electronics.

4.4.2 Target Radar Cross Section

For radar applications, the incident power density W_i affects the power that is reflected to a monostatic receiver that is colocated with the transmission antenna. The amount of reflected power is proportional to the radar cross section of a given target that is within the radiation beam pattern of the transmission system. The target radar cross section (RCS) is typically denoted using the symbol σ, and has the units of the reciprocal of length squared. The RCS of a given target characterizes its ability to reflect radar energy back the transmitter. The RCS is generally a function of the spherical azimuthal angle ϕ and the spherical elevation angle θ relative to a coordinate system that is centered on the target, so that the notation $\sigma(\theta, \phi)$ is often used. It is also a function of the radar frequency.

This RCS pattern depends upon the polarization of the incident and received polarizations, so that the notations $\sigma_{HH}(\theta, \phi)$ and $\sigma_{VV}(\theta, \phi)$ are often seen in analyses and measurements. Here, the former denotes the RCS of transmitting horizontally polarized radar waveforms and receiving horizontally polarized radar waveforms as well. The latter denotes the RCS obtained if vertically polarized waveforms are transmitted and received.

The RCS characterizes the ability of a target to backscatter or reflect impinging radar power at a set of angles $\{\theta, \phi\}$. This ability to backscatter is related to the electronic size of a given target, which is not necessarily related to the physical size of a target. Relatively large physical targets can have a relatively small electronic size, as characterized by its RCS. Methods involved in understanding target RCS are described in detail by Jenn [15].

4.4.3 EM Power Density for Monostatic Receiver

The use of a monostatic radar system involves a two-way link, where the first part of the link is comprised by the propagation of a radar waveform from the transmitter to a given target. The second part of the link is determined by the propagation of the radar echo that scatters off the target and then propagates from this target back to the radar receiver, which uses the same antenna front end as the radar transmitter. Both propagation directions of such a two-way link involve a separate $\{4\pi R\}^{-2}$ decrease in the power, giving an overall decrease in $\{4\pi R\}^{-4}$ for the two-way link.

The arguments above reveal that the incident signal power density arriving at a given target is given by W_i in (4.41). The target RCS σ is determined by the angles $\{\theta, \phi\}$ of the incident radar waveform relative to a coordinate system that is centered on the target. This target RCS gives the electronic size of the target and thus determines the total power P_s that is scattered back in the direction of the radar receiver antenna via:

$$P_s = W_i\sigma = \frac{P_tG_t}{4\pi R^2}\sigma \tag{4.42}$$

Next, the total power P_s that is scattered off the target must propagate a total distance of R between the target and the radar receiving antenna, thus giving another factor of $\{4\pi R\}^{-2}$ decrease in the power density that arrives at the receiving antenna:

$$W_r = \frac{P_tG_t}{4\pi R^2}\sigma\frac{1}{4\pi R^2} = \frac{P_tG_t\sigma}{\left\{4\pi R^2\right\}^2} \tag{4.43}$$

Finally, the total signal echo power P_r that enters the radar receiver antenna due to the subject radar scattering off a target is determined by the effective area A_{er} of the receiver antenna. As the nomenclature of the term aperture implies, the receiver antenna is equivalent to the opening through which EM waveform energy can enter the electronics of the receiver system. The main characteristic of an aperture is its cross-sectional area through which the scattered EM echo radiation enters. The effective area A_{eff} is typically relative to the true physical aperture opening area A by a scale constant factor ξ that incorporates the overall efficiency of the receiver antenna:

$$A_{\text{eff}} = \xi A \tag{4.44}$$

The expression for the total signal echo power P_r that enters the radar receiver antenna is equal to the product of the power density W_r that is incident at the radar receiver antenna and the effective aperture A_{er} through which EM radiation enters the receiver system:

$$P_r = W_r A_{er} = \frac{P_t G_t \sigma}{\left\{4\pi R^2\right\}^2} A_{\text{eff}} \tag{4.45}$$

The final form of the radar range equation is obtained by using a relationship between the effective area A_{eff} and the gain of the antenna receiver pattern. Generally, this antenna receiver power gain pattern $G_r(\theta_r, \phi_r)$ is a function of two angles $\{\theta_r, \phi_r\}$ relative to the coordinates of the receiver antenna. As with the transmission gain $G_t(\theta, \phi)$, we use the notation G_r to describe the value of angle-dependent gain pattern $G_r(\theta, \phi)$ in a direction of interest characterized by a spherical azimuthal angle $\phi_r = \phi_{r0}$, and a spherical elevation angle $\theta_r = \theta_{r0}$ relative to that of the receiver antenna. Next, the relationship between the receiver gain G_r and the effective receiver area A_{eff} is given by:

$$G_r = \frac{4\pi}{\lambda^2} A_{\text{eff}} \tag{4.46}$$

with λ equal to the radar wavelength. Substituting the expression for A_{eff} from (4.46) into (4.45) gives the final form of the two-way link of the radar range equation (RRE):

$$P_r = W_r A_{er} = \frac{P_t G_t G_r \sigma \lambda^2}{\{4\pi\}^3 R^4} \tag{4.47}$$

For 5G, LTE cellular, SATCOM, WLAN, and 6G communications systems, efforts include electronically steerable and multibeam antennas based on the desired signal-to-noise ratio. Hence,

$$SNR = \frac{P_S}{P_N} = \frac{P_t G_t G_r \sigma \lambda^2}{\{4\pi\}^3 R^4 k T_0 B F_n L} \tag{4.48}$$

where k is Boltzmann's constant of 1.38×10^{-23} w/(Hz°K), T_0 denotes a reference temperature in degrees Kelvin (°K). Also, $T_0 =$ 290°K approximates to give $kT_0 = 4 \times 10^{-21}$ w/Hz, B is the effective noise bandwidth (Hz) of the signal, F_n is the signal noise figure and is dimensionless, and L is a term included to account for all losses that must be considered when using the radar range equation. Note that L accounts for losses that apply to the signal in the sensing and communications and not the noise, such as those related to the sensor, the environment, and target (SET) operating conditions.

Substituting (4.46) into (4.48) provides a signals comparison for the antenna selections in the radar sensing and communication, specifically for the bandwidth comparisons for different wavelengths associated with 5G and beyond (e.g., THz for 6G),

$$SNR = \frac{P_t A_t A_{\mathrm{eff}} \sigma}{\{4\pi\} R^4 k T_0 B F_n L \lambda^2} \tag{4.49}$$

Using the relationship of frequency to wavelength ($f = c/\lambda$) can determine the changes in radar and communications. For example, new approaches can be compared: 4G LTE ($f < 6$Hz), 5G (mmWave 30 GHz $\leq f \leq$ 300 GHz), and smaller wavelengths of 6G (100 GHz $\leq f \leq$ 3 THz). The distances R for high G will be smaller with larger atmospheric loss, smaller wavelengths, and smaller antenna areas. Future antenna technology to serve multiple frequencies will include antenna arrays, beam steering, and multi-input multi-output technology to meet high bandwidth B requirements for the same SNR requirements.

4.5 Summary

The collection of important EM signals depends on the generation, propagation, and reception of EM waveforms via Maxwell's equations. The actual form of the EM radiation can have various polarizations, including linear, elliptical, and circular. The actual EM waveforms are generated by flowing charge carriers that excite the EM fields of the transmission system, thereby yielding radar waveforms that propagate into the surrounding medium. A type of pure magnetic dipole concept offers an exact solution of Maxwell's equations, so that the resulting EM fields and the Poynting vector describing radiative power flow are known exactly for all space. The resulting radiation power pattern is independent of the spherical azimuthal angle and depends on the square of the sine of the spherical elevation angle, just as it applies for electric dipole antennas. The radar range equation quantifies the propagation of a waveform emanating from a transmission radar system and scattering off a given target and propagating back to the radar receiver antenna.

References

[1] Sander, K. F., and Reed, G. A. L., *Transmission and Propagation of Electromagnetic-Waves*, Second Edition, New York: Cambridge University Press.

[2] Balanis, C. A., *Antenna Theory, Analysis and Design*, Fourth Edition, Hoboken, New Jersey: John Wiley and Sons, 2016.

[3] http://hyperphysics.phy-astr.gsu.edu/hbase/phyopt/polclas.html#c2.

[4] Garren, D. A., "Pure Dipole Radiation Via Exact Solution of Maxwell's Equations with Spherical Source Electric Current Density," *IET Radar, Sonar & Navigation*; Vol. 15, Issue 5, May 2021, pp. 1803–1814. First published online April 2, 2021; DOI: 10.1049/rsn2.12054. Available online from Wiley via Open Access: https://doi.org/10.1049/rsn2.12054.

[5] Garren, D. A., "Radiation Properties of Pure Magnetic Dipole Antenna with Spherical Current Density Via Exact Maxwell Solution," in *IEEE Transactions on Antennas and Propagation*, Vol. 70, No. 5, May 2022, pp. 3469–3476, DOI: 10.1109/TAP.2021.3137470.

[6] Curto, S., and Ammann, M. J., "Circular Loop Antenna Operating at 434 MHz for Medical Applications: Loop-Tissue Interaction," *IET Irish Signals and Systems Conference* (ISSC 2006), Dublin, Ireland, June 28–30, 2006, pp. 327–331.

[7] Foster, D, "Loop Antennas with Uniform Current," *Proceedings of the I.R.E.*, October 1944, pp. 603–607.

[8] Greene, F. M., "The Near-Zone Magnetic Field of a Small Circular-Loop Antenna," *Journal of Research of the National Bureau of Standards—C. Engineering and Instrumentation*, Vol. 71C, No. 4, October 1967, pp. 319–326.

[9] Ali Hamed, S. M., and Abbas, M. A. H., "Radiation from a Circular Loop Antenna Placed Coaxially Relative to a Conducting Body of Revolution," *IEEE Transactions on Antennas and Propagation*, Vol. 60, No. 10, October 2012, pp. 4937–4940.

[10] Ali Hamed, S. M., "Exact Field Expressions for Circular Loop Antennas Using Spherical Functions Expansions" *IEEE Transactions on Antennas and Propagation*, Vol 61, No. 6, June 2013, pp. 2956–2963.

[11] Ali Hamed, S. M., "Response to 'Comments on' Exact Field Expressions for Circular Loop Antennas Using Spherical Functions Expansions," *IEEE Transactions on Antennas and Propagation*, Vol. 62, No. 8, August 2014, pp. 4434–4435.

[12] Harrington, R. F., and Mautz, J. R., "Computation of Green's Functions for Bodies of Revolution," Bedford, Massachusetts: USAF Cambridge Research Laboratories, Scientific Report No. 6; Contract No. F19628-68-C-0180; AFCRL-70-0393, July 1970.

[13] Harrington, R. F., and Mautz, J. R., "Green's Functions for Surfaces of Revolution," *Radio Science*, Vol. 7, No. 5, May 1972, pp. 603–611.

[14] Harrington, R. F., *Time-Harmonic Electromagnetic Fields*, New York: John Wiley and Sons, 2001.

[15] Jenn, D. C., *Radar and Laser Cross Section Engineering, American Institute of Aeronautics and Astronautics, Inc.*, Reston, Virginia, 2005.

[16] https://upload.wikimedia.org/wikipedia/commons/7/74/Sidelobes_en.svg.

[17] Overview on Multipattern and Multipolarization Antennas for Aerospace and Terrestrial Applications (hindawi.com), https://www.tutorialspoint.com/antenna_theory/antenna_theory_fundamentals.htm.

5

Geolocation

5.1 Introduction

5.1.1 Emitter and Collector Assumptions

This chapter explains the methods for determining the location of a signal emitter on the surface of the Earth. It assumes that there are one or more transmission antennas emanating RF signals into the open environment. The angle dependence of the antenna gain for this transmission can have many possible forms depending upon the specific antenna type. However, the Friis equation determines the signal power that can be collected by a receiver antenna. Again, this collection ability depends upon many factors including the gain pattern corresponding to the receiver antenna.

It also assumes that the emitter on the Earth's surface is transmitting a variety of possible signals with various possible modulation methods, including the use of spread spectrum techniques. An emitter can transmit at a center frequency and bandwidth such that line-of-sight waveform propagation is the dominant mode of signal reception. Furthermore, the signal receivers are typically in motion either on or above the Earth's surface.

5.1.2 Possible Vignettes

The primary vignette explored in this chapter is the use of several passive collectors of RF signals in an attempt to determine the location of an important emitter of interest. For example, consider the example problem of attempting to locate a stranded individual who possesses an operation radio transmitter. For this scenario, it is assumed that global positioning system receiver information is not available to the stranded individual, who thus transmits a RF distress signal in hopes of being geolocated and then rescued.

The rescuers involved in the search effort operate two or more RF receivers to determine the unknown location of the stranded individual on the Earth's surface. For the use of TDOA, these receivers can be spatially fixed at various locations as well. If FDOA methods are applied, then at least one of the RF receivers must be moving while the stranded individual's transmitter is emanating RF signals. Then, the collected receiver data is sent to either one of the receiver stations or to another location for signal processing to compute the unknown transmitter location. It is also possible that this geolocation estimation process continues as more receiver signal measurements are collected, resulting in a continuously improving estimate of the unknown emitter's position.

5.2 Angle of Arrival Methods

In this section, we present the concepts of uncooperative geolocation of various transmitters/emitters from unknown locations. In the signal processing literature, this approach is known as an AoA or directional-of-arrival (DoA) problem. Transmitted electromagnetic energies from various sources can be dispersed by a directive antenna or omnidirectional antenna. A model can be developed to characterize/detect the signals of interests. A transmitting source could be a single-point source or multiple sources (i.e., the number of transmitting sources can be represented as 1, 2, 3,…., n). It is assumed that number n of sources is known. If n is unknown, then advanced detection strategy can be applied to identify these sources. Similarly, signal receivers can be of single or multiple (i.e., the number of received signal can be 1, 2, 3,…, m) of them. Figure 5.1 illustrates a typical AoA/DoA setting for this problem. Here, Tx represents transmitting/emitting signals or sources from 1, 2, 3,…, n of them; Rx represents receiving sources/received sensors from

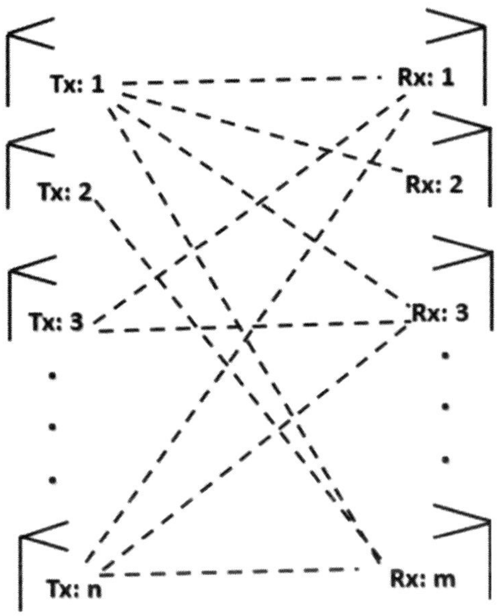

Figure 5.1
The angle of arrival or direction of arrival problem.

1, 2, 3,..., *m* of them. One Rx may find multiple Tx sources or multiple Rx may be used to find one or more Tx sources.

There are many books written to cover the analysis of AoA/DoA problems and solutions [1–3]. The description here followed the textbook written by Stoica and Moses [1]. Hence, readers are encouraged to seek this book for further discussion on the AoA/DoA geolocation problem.

5.2.1 Array Model for AoA/DoA Estimation

Consider $x(t)$ be the transmitted signal at a time t. If it takes τ_r time to travel the signal at receiver ($r = 1, 2, 3, \ldots, m$), then the output at a sensor r can be written as:

$$y_r(t) = h_r\,(t) * x(t - \tau_r) + n_r(t) \tag{5.1}$$

where $h_r(t)$ is impulse response, $*$ is the convolution n_r, and (t) is the additive or thermal noise. Here it is assumed that we know the impulse response $h_r(t)$. On the other hand, the signal $x(t)$ and time delay τ_r are unknown. So, the solution to the AoA/DoA problem is estimating the time delay for an unknown signal.

Now, the Fourier transform of $x(t)$ can be written as:

$$X(\omega) = \int_{-\infty}^{\infty} x(t)e^{-i\omega t}\, dt \tag{5.2}$$

Thus, inverse transform can be written as:

$$x(t) = \frac{1}{2\pi}\int_{-\infty}^{\infty} X(\omega)e^{i\omega t}\, d\omega \tag{5.3}$$

Hence, the Fourier transform of (5.1) can be written as:

$$Y_r(\omega) = H_r(\omega)X(\omega)e^{-i\omega\tau_r} + n_r(\omega) \tag{5.4}$$

where $n_r(\omega)$ is the uncertainty. Let, the signal $s(t)$ be the baseband signal for $x(t)$, and we can get $x(t)$ from $s(t)$ by modulation and demodulation process.

For the carrier frequency ω_c, the spectrum $X(\omega)$ can be written in terms of the signal spectrum $S(\omega)$:

$$X(\omega) = S(\omega - \omega_c) + S^*\left(-(\omega + \omega_c)\right) \tag{5.5}$$

It can be shown that the time domain signal is:

$$x(t) = s(t)e^{i\omega_c t} + \left[s(t)e^{i\omega_c t}\right]^* \tag{5.6}$$

$$x(t) = 2\,\mathrm{Re}\left[s(t)e^{i\omega_c t}\right] \tag{5.7}$$

$$x(t) = 2\alpha(t)\cos\left(\omega_c t + \vartheta(t)\right) \tag{5.8}$$

Here, $\alpha(t)$ and $\vartheta(t)$ are the amplitude and phase, respectively, of the signal $s(t)$ that can be written as:

$$s(t) = \alpha(t)e^{i\vartheta(t)} \tag{5.9}$$

Hence, (5.4) can be written as:

$$Y_r(\omega) = H_r(\omega)[S((\omega - \omega_c) + S^*(-\omega - \omega_c)]e^{-i\omega\tau_r} + n_r(\omega) \tag{5.10}$$

With lowpass filter processing, (5.10) can be written as:

$$Y_r(\omega) = H_r(\omega + \omega_c)S(\omega)e^{-i(\omega+\omega_c)\tau_r} + n_r(\omega + \omega_c) \tag{5.11}$$

For narrowband signals, (5.11) can be written as:

$$Y_r(\omega) = H_r(\omega_c)S(\omega)e^{-i\omega_c\tau_r} + n_r(\omega + \omega_c) \tag{5.12}$$

In the time-domain, (5.11) can be written as:

$$y_r(t) = H_r(\omega_c)s(t)e^{-i\omega_c\tau_r} + n_r(t) \tag{5.13}$$

5.2.2 Array Transfer Vector

The array transfer vector, $a(\theta)$, is also known as the direction vector, and it can be written as:

$$a(\theta) = \left[H_1(\omega_c)e^{-i\omega_c\tau_1} \ldots H_m(\omega_c)e^{-i\omega_c\tau_m}\right]^T \tag{5.14}$$

Here, θ corresponds to direction of arrival for the transmitting sources. It is assumed that we know the transfer characteristics and positions of the received sensors. Hence, (5.13) is a function of θ. Thus from (5.14), (5.13) can be written as:

$$y(t) = a(\theta)s(t) + n(t) \tag{5.15}$$

where $y(t) = [y_1(t) \ldots y_m(t)]^T$ is the array's output vector and $n(t) = [n_1(t) \ldots n_m(t)]^T$ is the noise vector.

By having a closer look, the impact of θ can be coming from two sources: the time delay τ_r and the transfer function $H_r(\omega_c)$. If the sensors/receivers are omnidirectional, then the transfer functions are independent of θ. If the sensors are identical, then the $H_r(\omega_c)s(t)$ can be written as $s(t)$. Then, (5.14) can be written as:

$$a(\theta) = \left[\ 1 \quad e^{-i\omega_c\tau_2} \ldots e^{-i\omega_c\tau_m}\ \right]^T \tag{5.16}$$

Since the receive sensors are linear elements, by applying the superposition principle, we can write:

$$y(t) = \left[a(\theta_1)\ldots a(\theta_n)\right]\begin{bmatrix} s_1(t) \\ \vdots \\ s_n(t) \end{bmatrix} + n(t) = As(t) + n(t) \tag{5.17}$$

Here, θ_r is the AoA/DoA for the rth source/transmitter/emitter, and $s_r(t)$ is the signal corresponding to the rth source/transmitter/emitter.

5.2.3 Uniform Linear Array for AoA/DoA Estimation

Figure 5.2 below is a visual depiction of a uniform linear array (ULA) where an array of m identical and uniformly spaced received

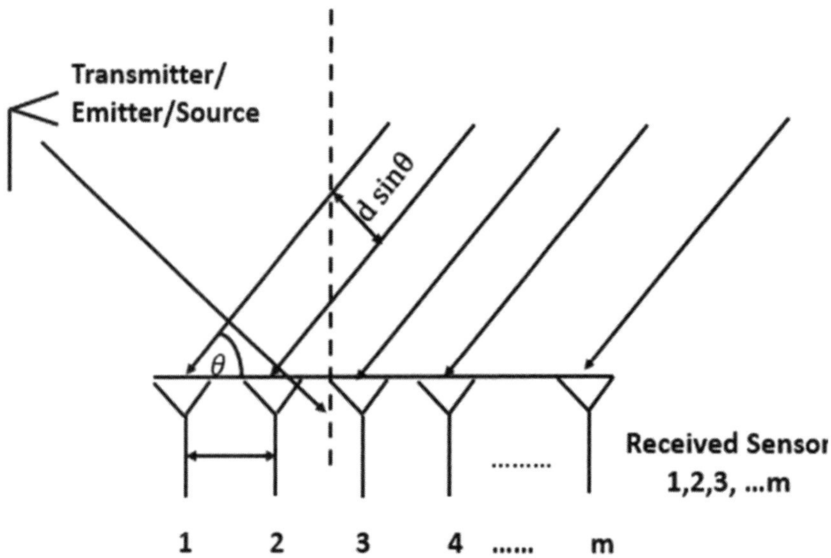

Figure 5.2
Configuration of a uniform linear array.

sensors are situated on a line. The distance between two consecutive sensors is d, and θ is the AoA/DoA of the signal radiating array.

If the signal waveforms are planar (i.e., the far-field assumption) and if the first received sensor be the reference point, then the time τ_r needed for the signal to travel from reference point to sensor r can be written as:

$$\tau_r = (r-1)\frac{d\sin\theta}{c} \tag{5.18}$$

where c is the speed of light and $\theta \in [-90°, 90°]$. Putting (5.18) into (5.16) gives:

$$a(\theta) = \left[1, e^{-i\omega_c d\sin\theta/c}, \ldots, e^{-i(m-1)\omega_c d\sin\theta/c}\right]^T \tag{5.19}$$

From (5.18), it can be shown that a limitation of the ULA approach is that the AoA (i.e., θ) must lie within a certain span of angles (i.e., [−90 to 90] degrees). Thus, if two transmitters/emitters are at symmetric locations, then they may yield similar time delays and thus be indistinguishable from one another. Given that $\lambda = c/f_c$ and that $\omega_c = 2\pi f_c$, consider that the relation $f_s = f_c\,(d\sin\theta/c) = (d\sin\theta/\lambda)$ implies:

$$\omega_s = 2\pi f_s = \omega_c \frac{d\sin\theta}{c} \tag{5.20}$$

By applying (5.19) into (5.18), we can write a final form for the direction vector:

$$a(\theta) = \left[\, 1 \;\; e^{-i\omega_s} \ldots e^{-i(m-1)\omega_s} \,\right]^T \tag{5.21}$$

5.3 Time Difference of Arrival Methods

At a very basic and fundamental level, the methods of determining the geolocation of an emitter are based upon the constancy of the speed of propagation of RF waveforms from the transmitter to the various receivers [4]. The speed c of light gives this constant value for propagation of RF signals from the unknown transmitter location to the various available RF receivers [5]. The analysis presented here assumes that the unknown emitter location can be described using two parameters $\mathbf{r}_e = \{x_e, y_e, 0\}$ within a set of Cartesian ground plane coordinates $\mathbf{r} = \{x, y, z\}$. In many cases, the RF receivers have a nonzero altitude z above the ground plane of the Earth's surface.

5.3.1 Time of Arrival

As the simplest example, assume that there exists only a single RF emitter within the area of interest. Further assume that this emitter transmits a signal beginning at a time t_0. In addition, the leading edge of the signal is characterized by a rise time δ_{t_0} and follows from the bandwidth of the transmitted signal itself. Assume that the location of the first antenna phase center when it initially receives this time reference (e.g., the rise in the signal) is $\mathbf{r}_1 = \{x_1, y_1, z_1\}$. The time t_1 at which the first antenna receives the time reference t_0 is given by:

$$t_1 = t_0 + \frac{1}{c}\left\|\mathbf{r}_1 - \mathbf{r}_e\right\|^2 = t_0 + \frac{1}{c}\sqrt{\{x_1 - x_e\}^2 + \{y_1 - y_e\}^2 + \{z_1\}^2} \tag{5.22}$$

Assume that there also exists a second receiver that is at the spatial position $\mathbf{r}_2 = \{x_2, y_2, z_2\}$ when it first receives this same emitted signal reference at the time reference t_2; that is,

$$t_2 = t_0 + \frac{1}{c}\left\|\mathbf{r}_2 - \mathbf{r}_e\right\|^2 = t_0 + \frac{1}{c}\sqrt{\{x_2 - x_e\}^2 + \{y_2 - y_e\}^2 + \{z_2\}^2} \tag{5.23}$$

5.3.2 Difference of Time of Arrivals

In the defined vignette, the true emission time reference t_0 is not known, and yet it is necessary to process the received signal data in such a manner as to obtain an accurate estimate of the emitter location $\mathbf{r}_e = \{x_e, y_e, 0\}$ within the ground plane. However, the process of calculating the difference of (5.22) and (5.23) removes this dependence upon the unknown value of t_0, giving the TDOA:

$$\begin{aligned}\tau_{2,1} &\equiv t_2 - t_1 \\ &= \frac{1}{c}\left\{\sqrt{\left\{x_2 - x_e\right\}^2 + \left\{y_2 - y_e\right\}^2 + \left\{z_2\right\}^2} - \sqrt{\left\{x_1 - x_e\right\}^2 + \left\{y_1 - y_e\right\}^2 + \left\{z_1\right\}^2}\right\}\end{aligned} \quad (5.24)$$

As a reminder, the positions of the first and second receivers (i.e., $\mathbf{r}_1 = \{x_1, y_1, z_1\}$ and $\mathbf{r}_2 = \{x_2, y_2, z_2\}$, respectively), are assumed to be known. Thus, the right-hand side of (5.24) possess only the two unknown emitter ground plane coordinates $\{x_e, y_e\}$, the values of which are not uniquely determined based upon a single TDOA measurement. That is, the values of possible $\{x_e, y_e\}$ pairs that give a solution to (5.24) trace a contour (i.e., a line that is curved in general) within the ground plane, so that a unique emitter position is not specified based upon a single TDOA measurement. This contour that gives the locus of possible emitter positions is referred to as an *isochrone*, which literally translates as *equal time* [6].

For example, consider two moving RF antennas that receive a signal transmitted at an unknown time t_0 from an emitter of unknown location $\{x_e, y_e\}$ within the ground plane. Assume that the first antenna receiver is located at the position of $\mathbf{r}_1 = \{x_1, y_1, z_1\} = \{2,\ 31,\ 2\}$ km when the transmitted signal is received at a time of $t_1 = 47.2$ ns. Furthermore, assume that the second antenna receiver is located at the position $\mathbf{r}_2 = \{x_2, y_2, z_2\} = \{42,\ -27,\ 3\}$ km at the time of $t_2 = 113.9$ ns. Thus, (5.24) determines the TDOA isochrone for this received signal pair:

$$\begin{aligned}66.7 &= 113.9 - 47.2 \\ &= \frac{1}{c}\left\{\sqrt{\left\{-9 - x_e\right\}^2 + \left\{6 - y_e\right\}^2 + \left\{1\right\}^2} - \sqrt{\left\{4 - x_e\right\}^2 + \left\{23 - y_e\right\}^2 + \left\{3\right\}^2}\right\}\end{aligned} \quad (5.25)$$

5.3.3 Hyperbolic Isochrones

Equation (5.25) for this example gives a single equation in terms of the two unknown scalar variables, x_e and y_e. The current form is not conducive for providing a closed-form solution of one of these two variables in terms of the other. Such desired canonical forms can be obtained by selecting spatial coordinates within the ground plane where the origin is the midpoint between $\mathbf{r}_1$ and $\mathbf{r}_2$, and one of the coordinate axes lies along the line joining $\mathbf{r}_1$ and $\mathbf{r}_2$.

Such a coordinate selection enables the use of the standard form of a hyperbola.

A hyperbola is defined based upon the selection of two points called the *foci*. For the current isochrone application, the locations of the foci are exactly equal to the locations F_1 and F_2 of the two antennas when the transmitted signal is received by each collector. Consider a given point P on the hyperbola. Also, use the notation $|PF_1|$ to denote the distance between points P and F_1, and correspondingly use $|PF_2|$ to specify the distance between points P and F_2. Then, for every point P on a hyperbola, the difference between these two distances $|PF_1|$ and $|PF_2|$ is equal to a constant [7], as shown in Figure 5.3. Therefore, the locus of a hyperbola is, by definition, equal to the TDOA of a signal that is transmitted at an unknown time from an unknown location that is received by two antenna receivers.

The only additional distinction is that for TDOA analysis, the sign of $\tau_{2,1}$ in (5.24) determines whether the left or right curve in Figure 5.3 is valid. Specifically, if $\tau_{2,1}$ is positive, then the signal arrives at the second antenna located at F_2 at a time that is later than the reception of the signal at the first antenna location of F_1. This result is obtained because the unknown transmitter location is closer to the first antenna than the second antenna, so that the TDOA contour corresponds to the hyperbola curve on the right in Figure 5.3.

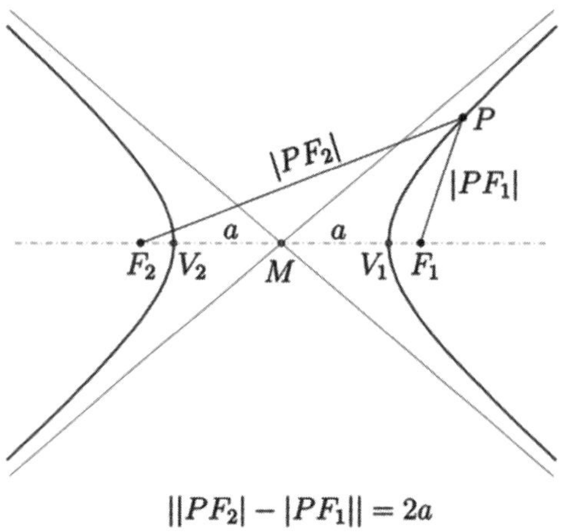

Figure 5.3
TDOA isochrone corresponds to hyperbola curves [7].

That is, the hyperbola curve on the left does not contain any possible points of the unknown transmitter location for this case of positive $\tau_{2,1}$.

The opposite result is obtained for the case of negative $\tau_{2,1}$, so that the transmitter is closer to the second antenna receiver at location F_2 than that of the first located at F_1. Thus, for this case, only the left curve of Figure 5.3 gives the locus of possible unknown transmitter locations, and the right portion of the hyperbola is not valid.

If the TDOA $\tau_{2,1}$ is exactly zero, then a degenerate case is obtained in which the unknown transmitter location is equidistant to both antenna receivers. This degenerate case gives a vertical line passing through the midpoint at M in Figure 5.3 as the locus of possible transmitter positions.

In full 3-D analysis, the locus of possible TDOA values corresponds to a hyperboloid of revolution about the axis joining the locations of the two antenna receiver locations. Again, the sign of the TDOA measurement determines whether only the right or left hyperboloid surface of revolution is retained in determining possible transmitter locations, which then is intersected with the ground plane to give the final locus of possible transmitter locations.

There exists an explicit mathematical relationship between TDOA measurement data and the form of the hyperbola is developed for the 2-D case in which the antenna receivers lie in the same ground plane as that of the unknown transmitter. The determination of the emitter position requires an additional set of received signals so that another TDOA measurement can be extracted. This additional TDOA measurement can be made from using these same RF receivers to collect another signal reference from this same emitter at $\mathbf{r}_e = \{x_e, y_e, 0\}$ at a later time, or this TDOA value can be obtained from another pair of RF receivers collecting this same original signal that was transmitted from the emitter at time t_0. The utility of this second independent TDOA measurement is that it similarly locates the 2-D unknown emitter position $\{x_e, y_e\}$ pairs along the locus of a second contour within the ground plane. However, the independence of the two TDOA measurements generally gives two different contours in the ground planes. Ideally, these two curves intersect at only one point in the ground plane, which should correspond to the true emitter position $\{x_e, y_e\}$ but also could have multiple or zero intersections as well.

5.3.4 TDOA Calculation Details

We return to the TDOA example that was defined in Section 5.3.2. Assume that there is an emitter at an unknown location within a 10-km radius circle centered at the origin of a ground plane coordinate system. Also assume that there are two moving RF receivers that receive a signal emanated from the emitter at an unknown time. Assume that the first receiver is at position $\mathbf{r}_1 = \{x_1, y_1, z_1\} = \{2,\ 31,\ 2\}$ km when the emanated signal is received at time $t_1 = 47.2$ ns, and the second RF receiver collects this same signal at time $t_2 = 113.9$ ns when it is at position $\mathbf{r}_2 = \{x_2, y_2, z_2\} = \{42,\ -27,\ 3\}$ km. Thus, the TDOA for this pair of RF collectors receiving the emitter signal is $\tau_{2,1} = t_2 - t_1 = 66.7$ ns.

As stated in the assumptions above, the actual start time of the emission is not known. Instead, it is assumed that correlation processing can be used to determine the temporal offset $\tau_{2,1} = t_2 - t_1 = 66.7$ ns between the receive times at the two receivers. Then, (5.23) is used with an additional scale factor of c, and the specific radar receiver motion parameters given above yields the following TDOA equation:

$$\begin{aligned} c\tau_{2,1} &= \sqrt{\{42 - x_e\}^2 + \{-27 - y_e\}^2 + \{3\}^2} \\ &\quad - \sqrt{\{2 - x_e\}^2 + \{31 - y_e\}^2 + \{2\}^2} \end{aligned} \tag{5.26}$$

Next, we examine the family of isochrones generated by (5.26), where there are different possible values for the TDOA $\tau_{2,1}$. Figure 5.4 shows such a family of isochrones, where the separation between adjacent curves each corresponds to a change in the TDOA value of 6.67 ns. For the scenario considered above, the actual TDOA is $\tau_{2,1} = t_2 - t_1 = 66.7$ ns. Figure 5.5 gives the individual isochrone for this TDOA value.

A single TDOA isochrone of Figure 5.5 does not yield the location of the emitter. However, assume that the two receivers move to new positions and that both receivers collect a signal from the same emitter again. Specifically, the first receiver lies at the position $\mathbf{r}_3 = \{x_3, y_3, z_3\} = \{23,\ 7,\ 2\}$ km when the emanated signal is received at time $t_3 = T + 37.6$ ns, and the second RF receiver collects this same signal at time $t_4 = T + 14.3$ ns when it is at position $\mathbf{r}_4 = \{x_4, y_4, z_4\} = \{-17,\ -11,\ 3\}$ km. Here, the value T is the time required for the

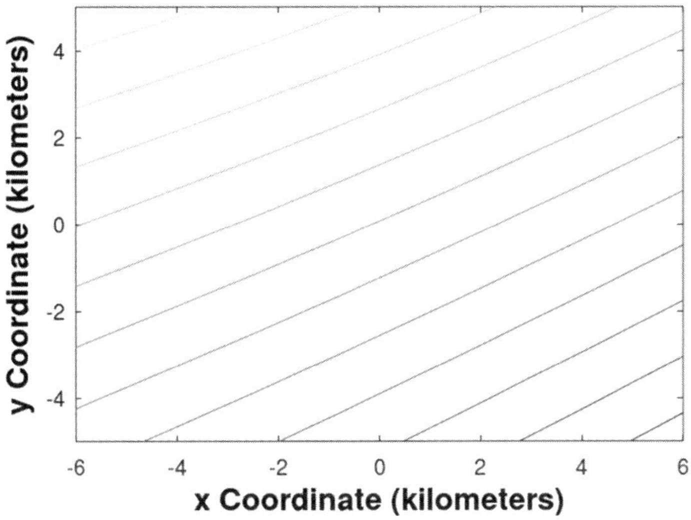

Figure 5.4
Family of TDOA isochrones corresponding to the initial set of signal measurements, as given by (5.26).

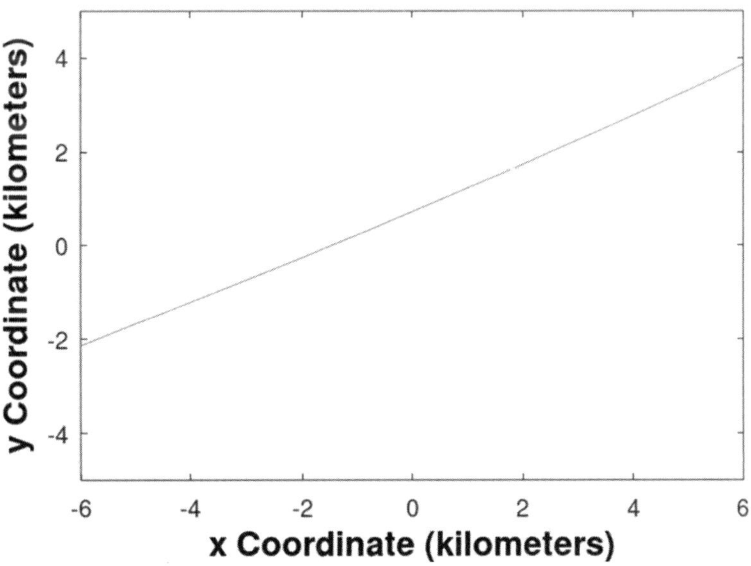

Figure 5.5
The single TDOA isochrone for the initial set of signal measurements, as given by (5.26) with $\tau_{2,1} = 66.7$ ns.

two receivers to move to their new positions. Thus, the TDOA for this pair of RF collectors receiving for emitter signal is $\tau_{4,3} = t_4 - t_3 = -23.3$ ns. The family of TDOA isochrones for this second set of signal measurements is determined by:

$$c\tau_{2,1} = \sqrt{\{-17 - x_e\}^2 + \{-11 - y_e\}^2 + \{3\}^2} - \sqrt{\{23 - x_e\}^2 + \{7 - y_e\}^2 + \{2\}^2} \tag{5.27}$$

Figure 5.6 shows this family of isochrones corresponding to the latter signal reception by the two receivers. Figure 5.7 presents the single isochrone for the specific TDOA of $\tau_{4,3} = t_4 - t_3 = -23.3$ ns. The intersection of the two single isochrones of Figures 5.5 and 5.7, correspond to the initial and latter signal collections. This intersection, as shown in Figure 5.8, lies at the position of the emitter's location on the surface, which is one methodology for using TDOA measurements to yield geolocation estimates. This graphical example provides an illustration of the basic concepts of TDOA geolocation.

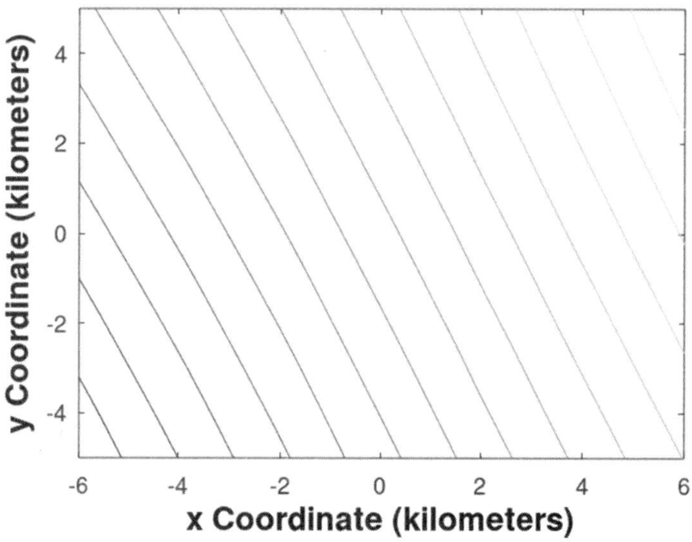

Figure 5.6
Family of TDOA isochrones corresponding to the latter set of signal measurements, as given by (5.27).

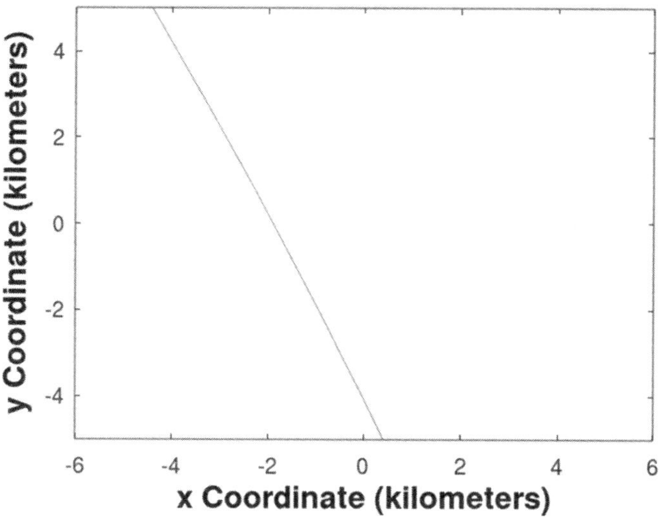

Figure 5.7
The single TDOA isochrone for the latter set of signal measurements, as given by (5.27) with $\tau_{4,3} = -23.3$ ns.

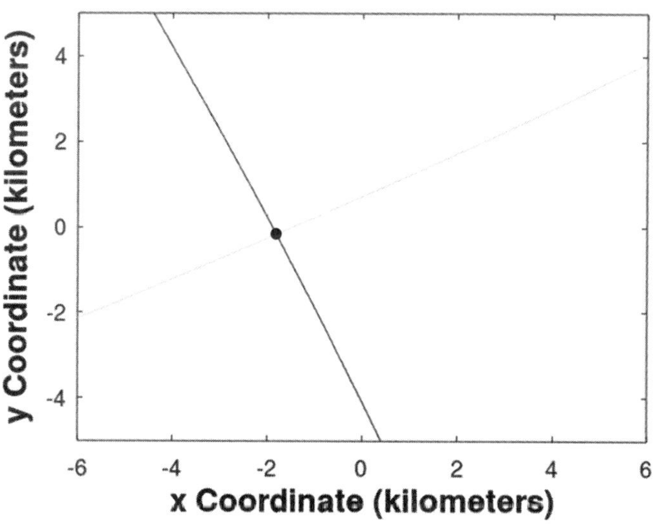

Figure 5.8
The intersection of the two single TDOA isochrones of Figures 5.5 and 5.7 gives the location of the emitter on the surface.

5.4 Frequency Difference of Arrival Methods

For practical applications, radar involves the propagation of EM waveforms where the relative line-of-sight velocity v between the transmitting and receiving antennas is much less than the speed of light c. Thus, nonrelativistic equations can be used in modeling the essential physical effects of the radar signal processing.

5.4.1 Doppler Frequency

One important effect is the Doppler shift in the frequency of the received signal relative to what was transmitted. Consider the case of a transmitting antenna that is emanating a narrowband EM waveform of frequency f. Next, assume that a receiving antenna is moving relative to the transmitting antenna with a LOS velocity v, where a positive value denotes an increasing separation between the two antennas as time marches forward. Then, the EM signal, as collected by the receiving antenna, is shifted by an amount relative to the original transmission waveform as given by:

$$f_D = -f\frac{v}{c} \tag{5.28}$$

The convention of including a minus sign in (5.28) is consistent with the lowering of the frequency for a receiver that is moving away from the transmitter, corresponding to *red shift* to lower frequencies. The opposite occurs for a receiver that is moving towards the transmitter, which gives a negative v and thus a positive Doppler frequency f_D.

For specific scenarios, mathematical calculations of the Doppler frequency are facilitated by using an alternate form of (5.28) that is defined in terms of the relative position vector $\mathbf{r}$ between the transmitting and receiving antennas, and the corresponding velocity vector $\mathbf{v}$ between the two antennas. Also, define φ to be the angle between the relative position $\mathbf{r}$ and velocity $\mathbf{v}$ vectors. Then, the Doppler frequency of (5.28) can be expressed as:

$$f_D = -\frac{f}{c}|\mathbf{v}|\cos(\varphi) = -\frac{f}{c}\frac{\mathbf{v}\cdot\mathbf{r}}{|\mathbf{r}|} \tag{5.29}$$

5.4.2 Difference of Doppler Frequencies

Next, consider the scenario is which there is a transmitting antenna on the Earth's surface that is emanating a RF waveform at the frequency f. Also, assume that there are two physically separated antennas that each receive this transmitted signal. Assume that Receiver #1 has a position of $\mathbf{r}_1$ and velocity of $\mathbf{v}_1$ relative to the transmitter. Likewise, the vectors $\mathbf{r}_2$ and $\mathbf{v}_2$ give the relative position and velocity, respectively, of Receiver #2 relative to the transmitting antenna. Then, the difference between the RF frequency collected by Receiver #2 and that of Receiver #1 is equal to the difference of the Doppler frequencies and can be expressed as:

$$\Delta f_{2,1} = f_{D,2} - f_{D,1} = -\frac{f}{c}\left\{\frac{\mathbf{v}_2 \cdot \mathbf{r}_2}{|\mathbf{r}_2|} - \frac{\mathbf{v}_1 \cdot \mathbf{r}_1}{|\mathbf{r}_1|}\right\} \tag{5.30}$$

The value $\Delta f_{2,1}$ is the FDOA between the two receiving antennas that have each collected the transmitted signal at frequency f. In general, (5.30) yields a FDOA iso-Doppler curve within the ground plane that delineates possible locations of the unknown emitter position $\mathbf{r}_e = \{x_e, y_e, 0\}$. These iso-Doppler contours have shapes that depend on the details of the relative positions and velocities of the two receiving antennas.

5.4.3 FDOA Calculation Details

As an example, use the same ground plane coordinates and notation as used in the TDOA example. Assume that the transmitting antenna is on the surface of the Earth at an unknown emitter location $\mathbf{r}_e = \{x_e, y_e, 0\}$. As in the TDOA example, the positions of the first and second receivers relative to the unknown transmitting location are given by the following, respectively:

$$\mathbf{r}_1 = \{x_1 - x_e, y_1 - y_e, z_1\} \tag{5.31}$$

$$\mathbf{r}_2 = \{x_2 - x_e, y_2 - y_e, z_2\} \tag{5.32}$$

Likewise, the velocities of these two receivers relative to that of the emitter have the following forms:

$$\mathbf{v}_1 = \left\{v_{x,1}, v_{y,1}, v_{z,1}\right\} \tag{5.33}$$

$$\mathbf{v}_2 = \left\{v_{x,2}, v_{y,2}, v_{z,2}\right\} \tag{5.34}$$

The specific values of the known receiver locations and velocities are used in (5.31) to (5.34) to give an equation for the unknown emitter position parameters in (5.30). That is, (5.30) determines a locus of possible emitter positions $\{x_e, y_e\}$ corresponding to the measured FDOA between the two receiver collectors. This locus is generally a curve within the ground plane, the shape of which is determined by the details of the relative positions and velocities of the two receiving antennas. Therefore, this FDOA measurement must be combined with other FDOA measurements from either other collector pairs, or from the same collectors after moving to different positions at a later time in order to intersect the various curves to yield a point solution for the unknown emitter position. In addition, TDOA measurement pairs also can be used to yield isochrones with which the FDOA iso-Doppler measurements can be combined to yield a point location of the unknown emitter position $\mathbf{r}_e = \{x_e, y_e, 0\}$.

In some cases, the received signal has a frequency f, so that this variable is known. For other cases, this variable is not known, so that additional difference measurements must be obtained to find a solution for the emitter position. In other scenarios, the RF frequency emanated from the transmitter may not be known, so that the frequency f becomes another unknown of the problem set for which the various TDOA and FDOA measurements are applied to generate an estimate of the unknown emitter location.

The use of detailed mathematical analyses can be conducted using the uncertainties in the time and frequency measurements, which can be used to generate estimates of the positional uncertainty of the emitter position on the Earth's surface. Often, such analyses are conducted using multivariate Gaussian distributions, which yield hyperellipsoidal solutions for the positional uncertainty of the final emitter position. The intersection of such a hyperellipsoid with the ground plane gives an ordinary 2-D ellipse within the ground plane, which is centered about the point estimate of the emitter position. This 2-D ellipse can represent the uncertainty in the estimate of the emitter position.

5.5 Cross Ambiguity Function

The methods of TDOA and FDOA described above rely upon techniques for estimating the time difference and the frequency difference for an emitted signal as collected by two different receivers. It is possible to form a simultaneous estimate of both TDOA and FDOA for a given signal by applying the cross ambiguity function (CAF), as described by Stein [8]. For this application, define the variables τ and f to be the time difference and the frequency difference, respectively, between the signal streams $s_1(t)$ and $s_2(t)$ collected by two different receivers. Then, the CAF is defined by the following integral:

$$A(\tau, f) = \int_0^T s_1(t) s_2^*(t + \tau)\exp(-j2\pi ft)\,dt \tag{5.35}$$

The upper limit of integration T is a viable period for which the signal is analyzed. The signal streams $s_1(t)$ and $s_2(t)$ are complex-valued corresponding to the in-phase (I) and quadrature (Q) channels.

The peak in the value of the magnitude of the CAF (i.e., $|A(\tau, f)|$) with regards to the two independent variables of $\{\tau, f\}$ gives the possible values of the TDOA τ and the FDOA f corresponding to the two signal streams. Various methods can be used to find these optimal TDOA and FDOA values. Initially, exhaustive search methods can be applied to find the optimal TDOA and FDOA values by examining the values of the CAF $|A(\tau, f)|$ over a grid in $\{\tau, f\}$. Then, a refined grid about the coarse estimate can be applied to yield an improved estimate of the optimal TDOA and FDOA.

This methodology is an extension of standard cross-correlation function techniques, but the CAF is applied to accommodate possible differences in the Doppler frequencies due to different relative motions of the two receivers. The standard cross-correlation function $C(\tau)$ is defined via:

$$C(\tau) = \int_0^T s_1(t) s_2^*(t + \tau)\,dt \tag{5.36}$$

There are some benefits of using the CAF to estimate the TDOA and FDOA for two-signal streams. First, the methodology naturally yields estimates of the uncertainties of both τ and f, as these uncertainties are proportional to the widths of the peak of the CAF magnitude function $|A(\tau, f)|$. Second, these methods have an inherent interference rejection capability since differences in the details of the underlying signal streams $s_1(t)$ and $s_2(t)$ due to similar but nonidentical signals. This yields reduced peak heights within the $|A(\tau, f)|$ function in comparison to a case in which the details of both underlying signals are identical. Third, these methods can yield signal peaks even for cases in which the underlying signal streams apply pseudonoise direct sequence spread spectrum (DSSS) methods and the corresponding spreading codes are unknown to the receivers. In effect, this capability exists since the second signal stream effectively acts as a matched filter relative to the first.

5.6 Summary

This chapter described various methods for determining the location of an RF emitter on the surface of the Earth. First, AoA/DoA methods were introduced, which utilize array processing to steer a receive beam in the direction of maximum signal intensity. Second, the concepts of TDOA were explained based upon the collection of an emitted signal by two different collection receivers. Third, FDOA methods were used to exploit differences in both the relative position and velocity of two receiver antennas relative to that of the transmitter. Finally, the methods of CAF processing were described as a convenient means for estimating the TDOA and FDOA for the signal streams collected by two receivers.

References

[1] Stoica, P., and Moses, R., *Spectral Analysis of Signals*, Upper Saddle River, NJ: Pearson/Prentice Hall, 2005.

[2] Van Trees, H., *Optimum Array Processing*, Hoboken, NJ: John Wiley and Sons, 2002.

[3] Van Trees, H., *Detection, Estimation, and Modulation Theory*, Hoboken, NJ: John Wiley and Sons, 1968.

[4] Tas, V., "Optimal Use of TDOA Geo-Location Techniques Within the Mountainous Terrain of Turkey," master's thesis, Naval Postgraduate School, September 2021.

[5] Levis, C. A., Johnson, J. T., and Teixeira, F. L., *Radiowave Propagation*, Hoboken, NJ: John Wiley and Sons, 2010.

[6] https://en.wikipedia.org/wiki/Tautochrone_curve.

[7] https://en.wikipedia.org/wiki/Hyperbola.

[8] Stein, S., "Algorithms for Ambiguity Function Processing," *IEEE Trans. Acoustics, Speech, and Signal Proc.*, Vol. ASSP-29, No. 3, June 1981, pp. 588–599.

6

Signals Detection and Estimation

6.1 Introduction

This chapter is an overview of modern signals detection and estimation theory. Though numerous books have been written about various algorithms for signal detection and estimation, the sections here summarize several selected algorithms needed to understand fundamentals of signals collection. A key issue in signal detection and estimation algorithm is *noise*. The principal sources of noises are the transmission and receiver systems' electronics, operating environments, and intentional high-powered signals transmission. It is assumed that thermal noise from communication systems is measurable and can be calibrated to find actual received signal strength. The environment clutter, including multiple noise sources from operating environments, such as manmade structures, trees, and many others, adds complexity to signal detection and classification. Finally, intentional high-powered signals, known as *jammers* or *interference signals* are very hard to mitigate from signals collection. The algorithms for mitigating the impacts of jamming signals and thus measuring actual signals requires complex algorithm development.

6.2 Detection Theory

Detection theory is a well-established area in signal processing. Section 6.1 highlighted the basic terminology and fundamentals of signal detection concepts needed for signals understanding. This chapter presents an overview of signal detection and definitions, strategies involving decision rules, and the detection of signals in various noisy environments.

6.2.1 Signal Detection Terminology

Signal detection is the ability for a system or device to decide whether an event of interest has occurred or not. To determine more information (i.e., signal, feature, data) about that event (i.e., information extraction), one performs estimation. In detection and classification, the *estimator* is called a *decision rule*. Detection theory or decision theory is also known as *hypothesis testing*. In the algorithmic flow diagram in Figure 6.1, the parameter θ that we want to estimate could itself be a function, in which case θ is called a *functional*.

Consider a scenario in which a signal has been transmitted to determine the presence or absence of a target of interest (bus, truck, aircraft, etc.). The detector decides between two choices (target or no target) by analyzing the received signal:

$$\begin{aligned} H_0 &: z(n) = v(n) \\ H_1 &: z(n) = A + v(n) \end{aligned} \tag{6.1}$$

with H_0 corresponding to the case of target/aircraft not present, and H_1 giving the situation of target/aircraft present. Let $v(n)$ be

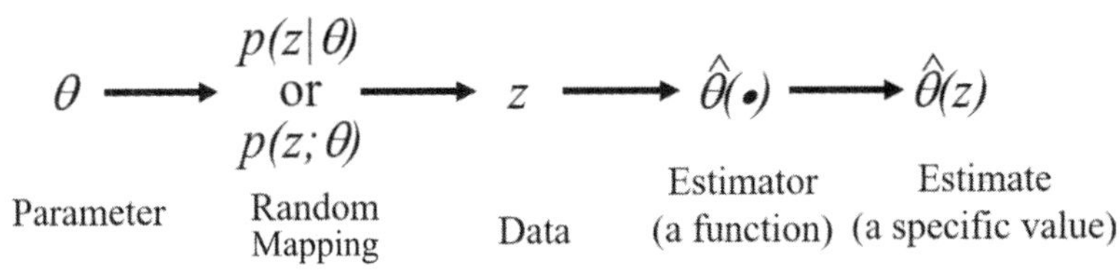

Figure 6.1
Algorithmic flow of the essential steps of signal estimation.

Gaussian with zero mean and unit variance. Then the probability density $z(n)$ under H_0 and H_1 are given by:

$$p\left(z(n) \mid H_0\right) = \frac{1}{\sqrt{2\pi}} \exp\left(\frac{-z(n)^2}{2}\right) \tag{6.2}$$

$$p\left(z(n) \mid H_1\right) = \frac{1}{\sqrt{2\pi}} \exp\left(\frac{-\left(z(n)-1\right)^2}{2}\right) \tag{6.3}$$

Then the likelihood ratio of (target present versus not) $\Lambda z(n)$ is given by:

$$\Lambda\left(z(n)\right) = \frac{p\left(z(n) \mid H_1\right)}{p\left(z(n) \mid H_0\right)} = \exp\left(z(n) - \frac{1}{2}\right) \tag{6.4}$$

By applying Bayes' rule, (6.4) can be written as the decision rule:

$$\exp\left(z(n) - \frac{1}{2}\right) \underset{H_0}{\overset{H_1}{\gtrless}} \frac{P(H_0)}{P(H_1)} \tag{6.5}$$

By applying a natural logarithm to the above equation, the log likelihood ratio is:

$$L\left(z(n)\right) = \left(z(n) - \frac{1}{2}\right) \underset{H_0}{\overset{H_1}{\gtrless}} \ln \frac{P(H_0)}{P(H_1)} \tag{6.6}$$

which then gives:

$$z(n) \underset{H_0}{\overset{H_1}{\gtrless}} \frac{1}{2} + \ln \frac{P(H_0)}{P(H_1)} \tag{6.7}$$

The decision rule in (6.7) states that if the received signal is stronger than a specified threshold, then a target is present; otherwise, the target is not there in the signal. The sample $z(n)$ is the test statistic. Figure 6.2 shows an example where the amplitude of the signal is raised when a target is present versus the case in which only noise is present. For example, at time measurement $n = 12$, the noise is $z[n] = 2.1$ and target and noise is $z[n] = 2.9$. To determine whether the signal is present or not, a probability density function (PDF) is constructed, along with a threshold to determine the difference between the signal and noise (Figure 6.3).

To analyze the PDF, some important terms and definitions follow to understand signal detection theory.

Binary hypothesis: In this radar example, the detector has to decide between H_1 and H_0. In this case, the set of hypotheses is characterized by $M = 2$, and hence this case is a binary hypothesis testing problem.

Multiple hypothesis: If $M > 2$, then the scenario is called *multiple hypothesis testing* or the *M-ary* detection problem.

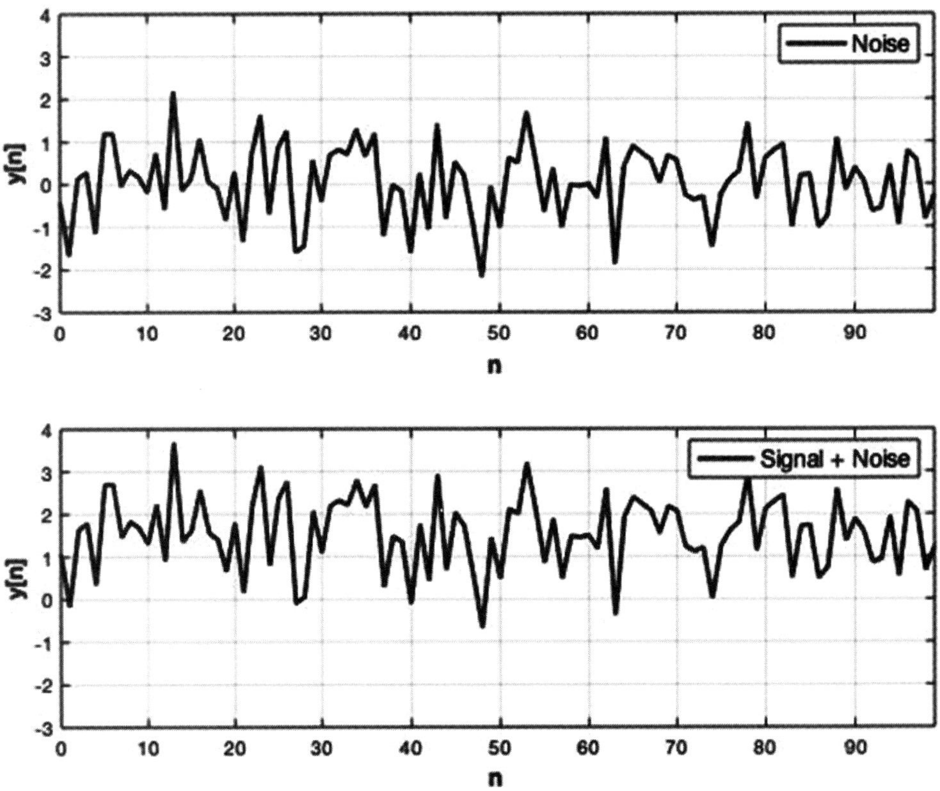

Figure 6.2
Comparison of noise-only versus signal-plus-noise cases.

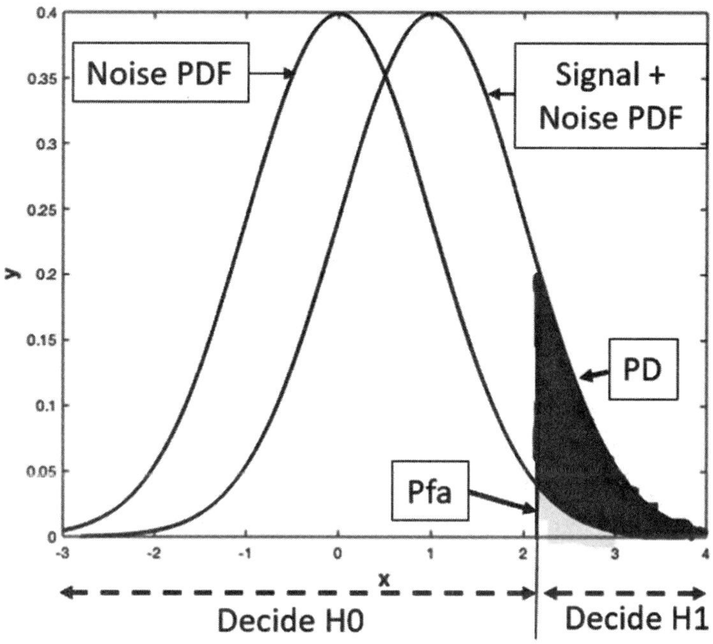

Figure 6.3
Signal and noise probability density function versus the noise-only PDF.

Observation/observation space: For each hypothesis, there is an observation (i.e., a random variable Z). The range of values that Z takes is called observation space. Note: Z is different than z.

Likelihood ratio test (LRT): The ratio of the density under hypothesis H_1 to the density under hypothesis H_0.

Receiver operating characteristic (ROC): A graph that shows probability of detection (P_D) against the probability of false alarm (P_{FA}). To generate a ROC curve, the following steps are used:

1. Generate M realizations of *noise* only and *signal* + *noise* data. Then compute the detection statistic for each realization.
2. For each threshold, count the number of threshold crossings of the test statistic for each realization.
3. Use the noise-only data and compute P_{FA} = number of threshold crossings divided by M.
4. Use the signal + noise data, compute P_D = number of threshold crossings divided by M.
5. Repeat steps 1, 2, and 3 for each threshold.

For additive white Gaussian noise (AWGN) data, assume the following:

$$H_0 : Z(n) = v(n)$$
$$H_1 : Z(n) = A + v(n), \text{ for } A = 0.2$$

which generates the ROC curve of Figure 6.4 based upon from the data in Figure 6.1.

In addition, Table 6.1 summarizes some of the important detection terminology used by statisticians and engineers.

6.2.2 Signal Detection Strategy

For any given decision problem, there are several decision strategies/rules that can be applied. Choosing the decision rule that is optimum is a function of the scenario. Four of the most common formulations are described in Table 6.2.

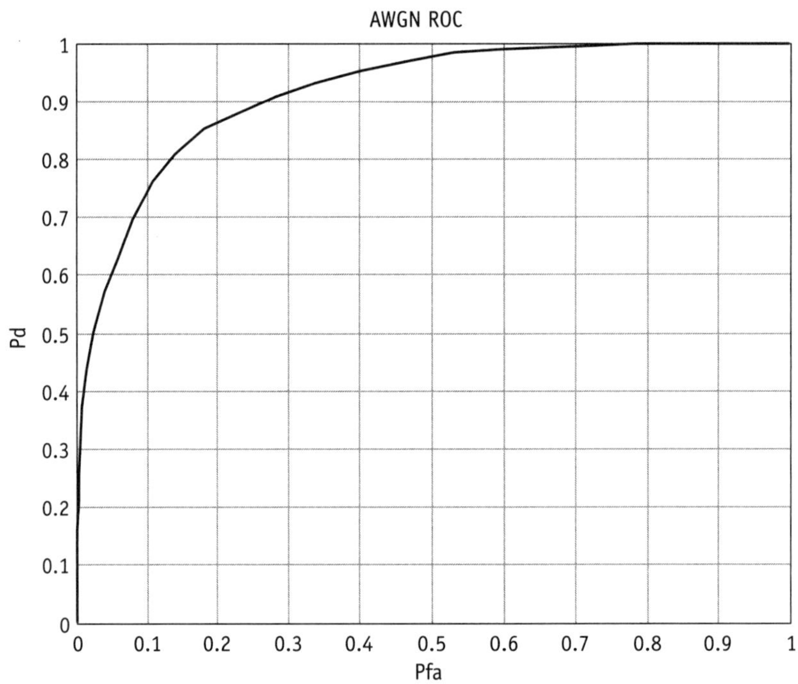

Figure 6.4
Example receiver operating characteristic curve.

Table 6.1
Detection Statistics

Test statistic ($T(x)$) and Threshold (γ)	Detector
Null hypothesis, H_0	Noise only hypothesis
Alternative hypothesis, H_1	Signal + noise hypothesis
Critical region	Signal present decision region
Type I error (decide H_1 when H_0 true)	False alarm FA
Type II error (decide H_0 when H_1 true)	Miss (M)
Level of significance or size of test (α)	Probability of false alarm (P_{FA})
Probability of Type II error (β)	Probability of miss (P_M)
Power of test (1-β)	Probability of detection (P_D)

Table 6.2
Decision Tests

Test	Prior Probability (P)	Cost (C)	Noise Power
Bayesian hypothesis testing	Known	Known	Known
Minimax criterion	Unknown	Known	Known
Neyman-Pearson test	Unknown	Unknown	Known
Constant false alarm test	Unknown	Unknown	Unknown

6.2.2.1 Bayesian Hypothesis Testing

Bayesian hypothesis testing (BHT) is used to design a detector when prior probabilities and costs/consequences of a decision are available. In radar detection, the consequences of a missed detection are typically much more dire than that of a false alarm. We can assign a cost C_{ij} when the decision is D_i and the hypothesis is H_j. Also, let $P(D_i, Hj)$ be the joint probability of the two. The decision rule seeks that the average cost or the risk is minimized. The average cost is given by:

$$\begin{aligned} C_{\text{Avg}} &= C_{00}P(D_0,H_0) + C_{10}P(D_1,H_0) \\ &\quad + C_{01}P(D_0,H_1) + C_{11}P(D_1,H_1) \end{aligned} \tag{6.8}$$

By applying Bayes' rule to the above equation, we get:

$$\begin{aligned} C_{\text{Avg}} &= C_{00}P(D_0 \mid H_0)P(H_0) + C_{10}P(D_1 \mid H_0)P(H_0) \\ &+ C_{01}P(D_0 \mid H_1)P(H_1) + C_{11}P(D_1 \mid H_1)P(H_1) \end{aligned} \tag{6.9}$$

Now, the conditional probability density is:

$$P(D_i \mid H_j) = \int_{z_i} f(z \mid H_j)\,dz \tag{6.10}$$

so that the average cost becomes:

$$\begin{aligned} C_{\text{Avg}} &= C_{00}P(H_0)\int_{z_0} f(z \mid H_0)\,dz + C_{10}P(H_0)\int_{z_1} f(z \mid H_0)\,dz \\ &+ C_{01}P(H_1)\int_{z_0} f(z \mid H_1)\,dz + C_{11}P(H_1)\int_{z_1} f(z \mid H_1)\,dz \end{aligned} \tag{6.11}$$

Minimum probability of error criterion and maximum a posteriori probability (MAP):

If we set $C_{00} = C_{11} = 0$ and $C_{10} = C_{01} = 1$, then the average cost becomes:

$$C_{\text{Avg}} = P(H_0)\int_{z_1} f(z \mid H_0)\,dz + P(H_1)\int_{z_0} f(z \mid H_1)\,dz \tag{6.12}$$

which is minimum probability of error. Then, the detection threshold becomes:

$$\eta\ (\text{or } \gamma) = \frac{P(H_0)}{P(H_1)} \tag{6.13}$$

Therefore, decision rule becomes:

$$\frac{f(z \mid H_1)}{f(z \mid H_0)} = \Lambda(z) \underset{H_0}{\overset{H_1}{\gtrless}} \eta = \frac{P(H_0)}{P(H_1)} \tag{6.14}$$

6.2.2.2 Minimax Criterion

In some situations, prior probabilities may not be available. However, costs to various decisions are available. Hence, there are strategies to design a detector under the circumstances of unknown probabilities. Using the Bayes solution corresponding to the value of $P(H_1)$ for which the average maximum cost is known as *minimax criterion*:

$$\eta \text{ (or } \gamma) = \frac{P(H_0)(C_{10} - C_{00})}{P(H_1)(C_{01} - C_{11})} \tag{6.15}$$

For the special case when $C_{00} = C_{11} = 0$ and $C_{10} = C_{01} = 1$, the minimax equation can be written as:

$$\eta \text{ (or } \gamma) = \frac{P(H_0)}{P(H_1)} \tag{6.16}$$

That is, minimax cost can be the average probability of error.

6.2.2.3 Neyman-Pearson Test

The Neyman-Pearson (NP) test is the design of a detector when prior probabilities and cost assignments are not available. In radar detection, the cost of misdetection of a target cannot be easily determined. Hence, the following approach is known as the Neyman-Pearson test:

Make P_{FA} as small as possible, but P_D as large as possible, although these are conflicting objectives.

Determine an acceptable P_{FA}, then maximize the P_D simultaneously.

The NP test is also known as most powerful (MP) test.

The following is the summary of the NP test:

- Maximize P_D for a given $P_{FA} = \alpha$.
- Insert observed data into the likelihood ratio.

- Compare to the threshold η (it should satisfy the false alarm rate inequality).
- If threshold exceeded, then declare the signal is present.

Example: Consider a radar operator looking for an aircraft. There are 10^6 pixels and a sweep rate of once every 4 seconds. We want a false alarm to occur no more than once every 6 hours. What is $P_{FA} = \alpha$?

Solution: In this case, the number of pixels viewed in 6 hours will be: $(6 \times 3600 \times 10^6/4)$ or 5.4×10^9. Therefore, required $P_{FA} < (1/5.4 \times 10^9) = 1.85 \times 10^{-10} = \alpha$.

6.2.2.4 Constant False Alarm Rate Detector

A common problem in detector design is a lack of knowledge of the noise power. This issue occurs since noise is generally unknown due to its environmental dependence. Noise can be time varying as well. Hence, the challenge is to design a detector that can constrain the P_{FA} without knowledge of the noise power. Technical approaches include the generalized likelihood ratio test (GLRT) and a scale invariant detector.

Assume that the likelihood ratio is $\Lambda(z) = \frac{1}{N}\sum_{n=0}^{N-1}\theta(n)$, such that the test decides that a signal is present if the following holds:

$$\Lambda(z) = \frac{1}{N}\sum_{n=0}^{N-1}\theta(n) = \theta_{\text{Avg}} > \eta \tag{6.17}$$

In this case, the test becomes:

$$T(\theta) = \frac{\theta_{\text{Avg}}}{\sqrt{\frac{1}{N}\sum_{n=0}^{N-1}\left(\theta(n) - \theta_{\text{Avg}}\right)^2}} > \eta \tag{6.18}$$

Then, θ_{Avg} will depend on noise variance; however, $T(\theta)$ will not, as it is scale invariant. The next section will focus on signal detection in noise.

6.3 Detection of Signals in Noise

Among approaches for improved signal detection, one strategy is to increase the signal-to-noise ratio (SNR). Mathematically, detection performance can be written as [1]:

$$d^2 = \frac{2NS^2}{\sigma^2} \tag{6.19}$$

Here d is the deflection coefficient, N is the number of samples, S is the signal, and δ^2 is the noise variance. By increasing integration time (i.e., by increasing the value of N), we can get better detection performance. Another approach is increasing the false alarm rate (FAR). If we increase FAR, then we generally select a low threshold value, and thus higher detection value. To optimize detection performance, a matched filter is used. The following section provides the matched filter concept.

6.3.1 Matched Filter

A matched filter is a linear filter. It is designed to yield maximum SNR at the receiver. Consider a signal represented as

$$x[k] = S + w[k] \tag{6.20}$$

where $w[k]$ is a zero-mean AWGN. If the signal is processed through a linear, time-invariant filter, at time $t = T$, then the sampler will output a signal part s_i and a noise part. Let the variance of the noise be δ_0^2. It can be shown that the SNR at time T is:

$$\left(\frac{S}{N}\right)_T = \frac{s_i^2}{\sigma_o^2} \tag{6.21}$$

The signal $s_i(t)$ can be expressed in terms of filter transfer function $H(f)$, where the signal's Fourier transform $S(f)$ is:

$$s_i(t) = \int_{-\infty}^{\infty} H(f)S(f)e^{j2\pi ft}\, df \tag{6.22}$$

Also, the noise power δ_0^2 can be expressed as:

$$\sigma_0^2 = \frac{N_0}{2}\int_{-\infty}^{\infty}\left|H(f)\right|^2 df \tag{6.23}$$

where the two-sided power spectral density of the input noise is $N_0/2$ watts/hertz.

Hence, the SNR can be expressed as:

$$\left(\frac{S}{N}\right)_T = \frac{2}{N_0}\frac{\left|\int_{-\infty}^{\infty} H(f)S(f)e^{j2\pi ft}\, df\right|^2}{\int_{-\infty}^{\infty}\left|H(f)\right|^2 df} \tag{6.24}$$

By using Schwarz inequality, it can be shown that maximum SNR at time T is:

$$\left(\frac{S}{N}\right)_T = \frac{2\int_{-\infty}^{\infty}\left|S(f)\right|^2 df}{N_0} = \frac{2E}{N_0} \tag{6.25}$$

Here, the signal energy E is written as:

$$E = \int_{-\infty}^{\infty}\left|S(f)\right|^2 df \tag{6.26}$$

From the above SNR derivation, it is understood that achieving maximum SNR depends on energy of the input signal and power spectral density of the noise. Maximum SNR does not depend on a particular waveform.

6.3.2 Matched Filter: Correlator and Convolution

The impulse response of the matched filter is the delayed, mirrored image of the transmitted waveform. If the transmitted signal is $s(t)$, then the mirrored and delayed signal can be expressed as $s(-t)$ and $s(T - t)$, respectively. If the received signal is $r(t)$, and impulse response is $h(t)$, then we can write the output signal as

$$y(t) = r(t) * h(t) = \int_0^t r(\tau)h(t-\tau)\,d\tau$$
$$= \int_0^t r(\tau)s(T-(t-\tau))\,d\tau$$
$$y(T) = \int_0^T r(\tau)s(\tau)\,d\tau, \quad \text{when } t = T \tag{6.27}$$

The output signal above is the *correlation* of $r(t)$ with $s(t)$. The mathematical operation of the matched filter shown above is that of *convolution*. A matched filter is often known as a correlator. An important note is that the matched filter and correlator outputs are the same when the sample time $t = T$.

6.3.3 White Noise Versus Colored Noise

White noise is the noise signal whose power spectrum is flat (Figure 6.5). It will have almost constant integrated power at different frequency bands of same duration or bandwidth. Colored noise will have different integrated power at different frequency bands of the same duration/bandwidth.

6.3.4 Detection of Known Signals in White Noise

To detect known signals in white noise, a correlation receiver can be used, as shown in Figure 6.6. For a very simple implementation, it can be written as:

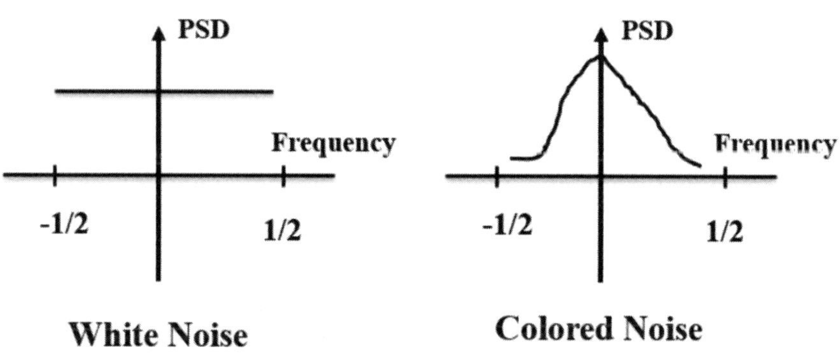

Figure 6.5
White noise versus colored noise.

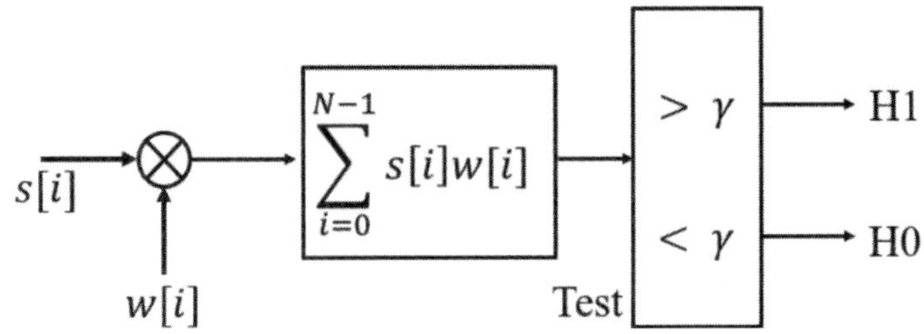

Figure 6.6
Replica correlator.

$$\sum_{i=0}^{N-1} s[i]w[i] > \gamma$$

Here $s[i]$ is the signal, $w[i]$ is the noise, γ is the threshold.

Example: Consider a known signal given by

$$s[i] = \begin{cases} 1, & \text{for } i = 0, 1, 2, \ldots 19 \\ -1, & \text{for } i = 20, 21, \ldots 39 \end{cases}$$

Figure 6.7 compares the corresponding samples for the cases of no signal and signal present. It can be shown that when a signal is present, the value of γ is very high compared to the noise-only signal.

6.3.5 Detection of Known Signals in Colored Noise

Detection of signals for scenarios in which the colored noise is characterized by a covariance function that is much more difficult. It involves expanding the observation space as a set of orthonormal basis functions. The functions are chosen so that coefficients of the expansion are uncorrelated. For details on this implementation, readers are encouraged to see [1–4].

6.3.6 Detection of Random Signals

There are situations when the signal is not completely known in WGN. In this case, the signal is modeled as a *random* process. For example, in an operating environment of a radar system, signals

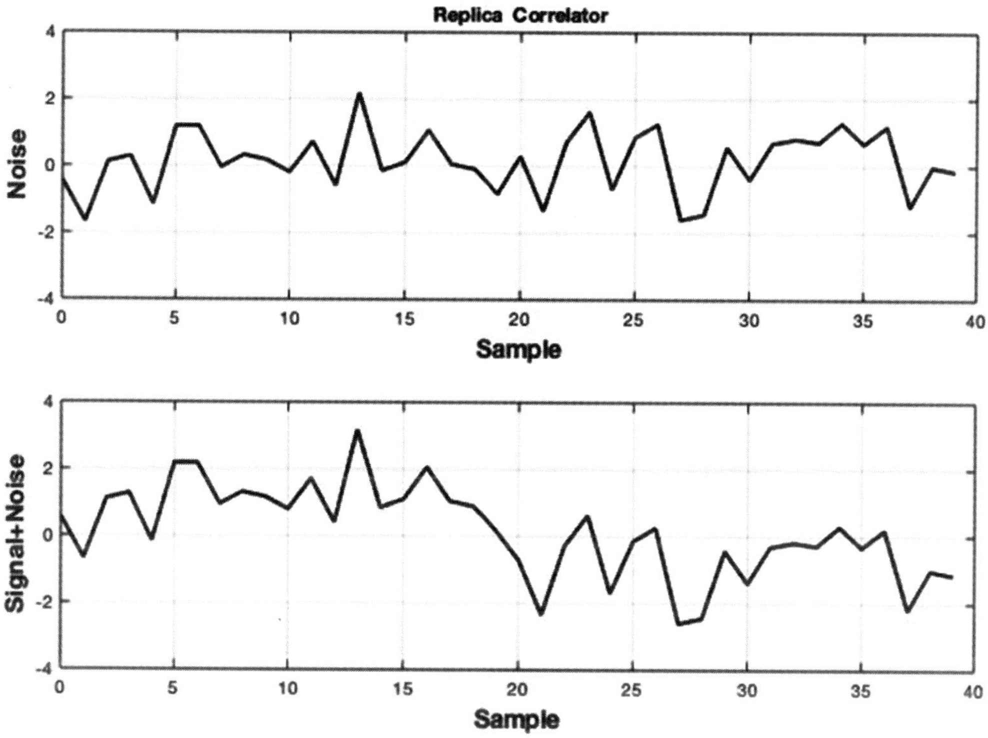

Figure 6.7
Detection of known signal with replica correlator.

are mixed with various noise sources and clutter. In this case, it is prudent to model the signal as a random process with known covariance. The algorithmic steps involve estimating the signal with a Weiner filter and then implementing a correlator, known as an *estimator-correlator*. Another name for this detector is *energy detector*. For more details on the random signal detection, see Kay [1].

6.3.7 Detection in Non-Gaussian Noise

Non-Gaussian noise has the characteristic of large spikes or outliers, which causes more false alarms than occurs for the Gaussian noise. A solution to the spiking problem is to develop an optimal detector that limits the data samples before applying matched filter. This type of detector is also known as a *locally optimum*, or *weak signal* or *threshold* detector.

6.3.8 Designing Detectors with Unknown Parameters

In some situations, the signal and noise probability density functions are not completely known. Hence, designing an optimal detector for these situations is challenging. Technical approaches for signal detection with unknown parameters include:

- Find an optimal detector, then plug in estimates of unknown parameters. This is known as *estimate and plug* detector.
- Use a Bayesian approach by assuming a priori PDF for unknown parameters.

6.4 Signal Parameter Estimation

This section presents concepts and algorithms for signal estimation. To compare signal detection with the estimation problem, the first involves finding a way to know the presence of a certain type of signal, and the latter applies details about the known parameters of the detected signal. For example, we may be interested in detecting radar signals in an environment (which includes nonradar signals such as Wi-Fi signals, Automatic Dependent Surveillance-Broadcast (ADS-B) signals, and many others). Once that signal has been detected, we need to know details such as frequency band, modulation, chirp or unchirped, and coding scheme, among others. In theory, signal parameter estimation techniques provide information regarding the detailed characteristics of the signal under investigation.

To estimate the parameters of a given signal, one must collect samples of that signal and develop a mathematical model based on the samples. It is assumed that we can verify the parameters from the received/detected signal by inspection or other ways based on the general parameters used to generate and transmit a signal. However, in real-world applications, parameters need to be estimated in real-time in an automated fashion. Hence, various estimation algorithms are developed that perform differently under various operating conditions. The performance criteria of various estimators has been developed and signal detection terminology has evolved; see [4, 6, 7].

As mentioned, to develop a good estimator, one must model the signal mathematically from the data. One way to describe signal data is by its probability density function as received signals are random. For the WGN model $w[n]$, the PDF is described as $N(0, \sigma^2)$, where the mean is zero and the variance is σ^2. Here, the parameters for WGN are often written as $\theta = [\mu, \sigma^2]^T$.

Consider a signal represented as

$$x[n] = S + w[n] \tag{6.28}$$

where $w[n]$ is a zero-mean Gaussian noise. Our goal here is to estimate the amplitude S of the signal based upon the measurement signals $x[n]$. Consider signals collected over time as:

$$\begin{aligned} x[0] &= S[0] + w[0] \\ x[1] &= S[1] + w[1] \\ x[2] &= S[2] + w[2] \\ x[N] &= S[N] + w[N] \end{aligned} \tag{6.29}$$

Then a good estimator for S can be the average of the collected signals,

$$\hat{S} = \frac{1}{N}\sum_{n=0}^{N-1} x[n] \tag{6.30}$$

To calculate the mean/expected value of this estimator, we find:

$$E\left(\hat{S}\right) = E\left\{\frac{1}{N}\sum_{n=0}^{N-1} x[n]\right\} = \frac{1}{N}\sum_{n=0}^{N-1} E\left(x[n]\right) = \frac{NS}{N} = S \tag{6.31}$$

To calculate the variance of this estimator, we find

$$\begin{aligned} \operatorname{var}\left(\hat{S}\right) &= \operatorname{var}\left\{\frac{1}{N}\sum_{n=0}^{N-1} x[n]\right\} = \frac{1}{N^2}\sum_{n=0}^{N-1} x[n] = \frac{1}{N^2}\left(N\sigma^2\right) \\ &= \frac{\sigma^2}{N} \end{aligned} \tag{6.32}$$

A key fact about developing estimators is that they are developed based on random phenomenon (i.e., noise) that are observed in the measured data, and hence, performance may vary slightly from one model to another. Also, the quality of the estimator may depend upon the collection of an adequate number of sampled signals, and it must be based on a sufficient statistic of the collected data. The following section provides important terminology used for signal parameter estimation algorithm development.

6.4.1 Minimum Variance Unbiased Estimation

When developing an estimator, typical approaches focus on the one that provides good performance on average. In other words, the goal is to find an estimator that is consistent. An estimator is unbiased if, on average, the estimator provides the true value of the unknown parameters. An unbiased estimator that has lower variance than any other unbiased estimator for all possible values of the parameter is called the minimum variance unbiased estimator (MVUE). Mathematically, an estimator is defined to be unbiased if the following holds:

$$E\left(\hat{\theta}\right) = \theta$$

That is, the expected value of the parameter θ is close to the true value of the parameter θ. In the previous example, $x[n] = S + w[n]$, we found that the sample mean was the expected value of the signal. Hence, the sample mean estimator is therefore an unbiased biased estimator.

To find a minimum variance unbiased estimator, we often design an optimal estimator based on mean square error (MSE). In this case, MSE is defined as

$$MSE\left(\hat{\theta}\right) = E\left[\left(\hat{\theta} - \theta\right)^2\right] \tag{6.33}$$

where $\hat{\theta}$ represents the estimated parameters, θ gives the true parameters, and E is the expectation operator.

6.4.2 Cramer-Rao Lower Bound

It is important to establish a lower bound of the variance of any unbiased estimator. The lower bound of an unbiased estimator whose variance is smaller than this is impossible to attain. The theory of Cramer-Rao lower bound (CRLB) allows us to determine if a given estimator attains the lower bound. Another way to express CRLB is that it provides a lower estimate for the variance of an unbiased estimator. Estimators that are close to the CRLB are less biased (i.e., more accurate to use).

Though the theory of CRLB can be found in various books, the definition and mathematical expression presented here follows from [1]. CRLB is stated as the case where the PDF $p(x;\,\theta)$ satisfies the condition:

$$E\left[\frac{\partial\{\ln p(x;\theta)\}}{\partial\theta}\right] = 0, \quad \text{for all } \theta \tag{6.34}$$

The variance of any unbiased estimator $\hat{\theta}$ must satisfy:

$$\text{var}\left(\hat{\theta}\right) \geq \frac{1}{-E\left[\frac{\partial^2\{\ln p(x;\theta)\}}{\partial\theta^2}\right]} \tag{6.35}$$

An unbiased estimator can be found as for all θ if and only if:

$$\frac{\partial \ln p(x;\theta)}{\partial\theta} = I(\theta)\left(g(x) - \theta\right) \tag{6.36}$$

The minimum variance unbiased (MVU) estimator is $\hat{\theta} = g(x)$, and the minimum variance is $1/I(\theta)$.

For the signal $x[n] = S + w[n]$ for $n = 0, 1, 2, \ldots N - 1$, the resulting CRLB for S is:

$$p(x;S) = \prod_{n=0}^{N-1} \frac{1}{\sqrt{2\pi\sigma^2}} \exp\left[-\frac{1}{2\sigma^2}\left(x[n] - S\right)^2\right] \tag{6.37}$$

By taking the first derivative, we get

$$\begin{aligned}\frac{\partial \ln p(x;S)}{\partial S} &= \frac{\partial}{\partial S}\left[-\ln\left[\left(2\pi\sigma^2\right)^{\frac{N}{2}}\right] - \frac{1}{2\sigma^2}\sum_{n=0}^{N-1}\left(x[n]-S\right)^2\right] \\ &= \frac{1}{\sigma^2}\sum_{n=0}^{N-1}\left(x[n]-S\right) \\ &= \frac{N}{\sigma^2}(\bar{x}-S)\end{aligned} \tag{6.38}$$

By taking the second derivative, we get

$$\frac{\partial^2 \ln p(x;S)}{\partial S^2} = \frac{-N}{\sigma^2} \tag{6.39}$$

Hence, $\mathrm{var}(\hat{S}) \geq \sigma^2/N$.

6.4.3 Maximum Likelihood Estimation

The maximum likelihood estimator (MLE) is a commonly used estimator. It is an optimal estimator for cases with a sufficient amount of large training data. In MLE, using the training data, one estimates the parameter value θ that makes the new data the most probable of a given signal or object class. The goal is to maximize the probability of obtaining the sample that has been observed.

Consider a PDF $p(x;\theta)$ that is specified by the parameters $\theta = [\theta_1, \theta_2, \theta_3 \ldots \theta_k]$. If $p(x;\theta)$ is $N(\mu, \sigma^2)$, then $\theta = [\mu, \sigma^2]$. Often, the notation $p(x|\theta)$ is used to represent a PDF $p(x;\theta)$ that depends on the parameters θ as opposed to the conditional density.

Consider $S = \{X_1, X_2, X_3, \ldots, X_N\}$ to be N independent samples of training data that are independent and identically distributed with the PDF is $N(\mu, \sigma^2)$. The likelihood of θ with respect to the set of samples S can be represented as:

$$p(S \mid \theta) = \prod_{n=1}^{N} p\left(x_n \mid \theta\right) \tag{6.40}$$

The MLE of θ is the value of θ that maximizes the likelihood function $p(S|\theta)$, which can be written as:

$$\hat{\theta} = \arg\max_{\theta}\{p(S \mid \theta)\} \tag{6.41}$$

It can be shown that there is similarity between maximum likelihood classifier and maximum likelihood parameter estimation. For the ML classifier, one can write:

$$\hat{C}_l = \arg\max_{\theta}\{p(X \mid C_i)\} \tag{6.42}$$

that is, decide class C_i that maximizes $p(X|C_i)$. In a sense, the ML classifier and the ML estimator apply the same theory to different problems. The following gives the essential steps of the MLE algorithm.

MLE Algorithm Implementation Steps

1. Consider a Gaussian with unknown μ or let $p(x|\mu)$ be $N(\mu, \sigma^2)$, where μ is unknown, and σ^2 is known.

2. $$\hat{\mu} = \arg\max_{\mu}\{\ln(\mu)\} = \arg\max_{\mu}\left\{\sum_{n=1}^{N}\ln\left(p\left(x_n \mid \mu\right)\right)\right\} \tag{6.43}$$

$$= \arg\max_{\mu}\left\{\sum_{n=1}^{N}\ln\left[\frac{1}{\sqrt{2\mu\sigma}}\exp\left(\frac{\left(x_n-\mu\right)^2}{2\sigma^2}\right)\right]\right\}$$

$$= \arg\max_{\mu}\left\{\sum_{n=1}^{N}\ln\left(\sqrt{2\pi\sigma}\right)-\frac{\left(x_n-\mu\right)^2}{2\sigma^2}\right\}$$

By taking a derivative with respect to μ, and setting to zero, we get:

$$\sum_{n=1}^{N}\frac{\left(x_n-\mu\right)}{\sigma^2} = 0$$
$$\sum_{n=1}^{N}x_n = N\mu \rightarrow \hat{\mu} = \frac{1}{N}\sum_{n=1}^{N}x_n \tag{6.44}$$

That is, the ML estimate of the mean μ is just the average value of the training data, which is very intuitive and understandable. Similarly, the MLE for Gaussian variance σ^2 can be computed as:

$$\widehat{\sigma^2} = \frac{1}{N}\sum_{n=1}^{N}\left(x_n - \hat{\mu}\right)^2 \tag{6.45}$$

6.4.4 Maximum A Posteriori Estimator

Bayes theorem can be expressed as:

$$p(\theta \mid x) = \frac{p(x \mid \theta)p(\theta)}{p(x)} \tag{6.46}$$

Here, θ is the model parameter *s* and is the observed data. Also, the following notation is used:

$$p(\theta \mid x): \text{ is the posterior}$$
$$p(x \mid \theta): \text{ is the likelihood}$$
$$p(\theta): \text{ is the prior}$$

This theory involves the likelihood (i.e., probability of data x given the model parameter θ, and $p(\theta \mid x)$) and uses the prior (i.e., which gives the belief about data before the data are collected) specifically, giving the distribution over parameters θ. The posterior is the result after observing data, giving the belief about the model to yield the posterior probability $p(\theta \mid x)$ after the data x have been observed.

In maximum a posteriori estimation, the algorithm's goal is to estimate the parameters $\hat{\theta}$ that maximize the posterior PDF, which is written as:

$$\hat{\theta} = \arg\max_{\theta} p(\theta \mid x) \tag{6.47}$$

If we know $p(x)$, our goal for MAP estimator becomes:

$$\begin{aligned}\hat{\theta}_{\text{MAP}} &= \arg\max_{\theta} p(x \mid \theta)p(\theta) \\ &= \arg\max_{\theta}\left[\ln p(x \mid \theta) + \ln p(\theta)\right]\end{aligned} \tag{6.48}$$

It is also noted that in general, from Bayes' theorem implementation: the world model of $p(x)$ must be reduced to a manageable set, such as a binary decision. If the prior $p(\theta)$ is known use the MAP; but typically this is not true as the prior distribution is not available. Most implementations of Bayes' is a MLE of $p(\theta\,|x)/p(x|\theta) \geq \eta$.

6.5 Summary

This chapter presented fundamentals of signal detection and estimation theory needed for signals collection and exploitation. Though various techniques presented here can be found in reference books published by the pioneers and educators in this field, our effort is to present some of the important concepts and algorithms needed for signals collection and analysis. As mentioned, readers are encouraged to search for other books for a deeper understanding of signal detection and estimation.

References

[1] Kay, S. M., *Fundamentals of Signal Processing, Volume II: Detection Theory*, Hoboken, NJ: Prentice-Hall, 1998.

[2] Peterson, W. W., Birdsall, T. G., and Fox, W. C., "The Theory of Signal Detectability," *IRE Professional Group on Information Theory*, Vol. 4, No. 4, September 1954.

[3] Srinath, M. D., and Rajasekaran, P. K., *An Introduction to Statistical Signal Processing with Applications*, New York: John Wiley and Son, 1979.

[4] Neyman, J., Pearson, E. S., "On the Problem of the Most Efficient Tests of Statistical Hypotheses," *Philosophical Transactions of the Royal Society of London. Series A, Containing Papers of a Mathematical or Physical Character*, Vol. 231, No. 694-706 (1933), pp. 289–337.

[5] Woodard, P. M., and Davies, I. L., "Information Theory and Inverse Probability in Telecommunication," *Proceedings of the Institute of Electrical Engineers*, Vol. 99, Part III, March 1952.

[6] Marcum. J. I., *A Statistical Theory of Target Detection by Pulsed Radar*, The RAND Corporation, December 1947.

[7] Gelfand, S., "ECE 645 Notes," Purdue University, Spring 2015, https://engineering.purdue.edu/ChanGroup/ECE645Notes/StudentLecture07.pdf.

[8] Reich, E., and Swerling, P., *On the Detection of Sine Wave in Gaussian Noise*, The RAND Corporation, June 1952.

[9] Wald, A., and Wolfowitz, J., "Optimum Character of the Sequential Probability Ratio Test," *The Annals of Mathematical Statistics*, Vol. 19, No. 3, September 1948.

[10] Poor, H. V., *An Introduction to Signal Detection and Estimation*, New York: Springer-Verlag.

[11] Van Trees, H. L., *Detection, Estimation, and Modulation Theory, Part I*, Hoboken, NJ: John Wiley and Sons.

[12] Middleton, D., *An Introduction to Statistical Communication Theory*, Peninsular Publishing Company, 1987.

[13] Skolnik, M. I., *Introduction to Radar Systems*, New York: McGraw-Hill, 2001.

[14] Richards, M., *Fundamentals of Radar Signal Processing*, New York: McGraw-Hill, 2005.

[15] Mahafza, B., *Radar Signal Processing and Analysis Using MATLAB*, Boca Raton, FL: Chapman and Hall/CRC, 2009.

[16] Hippenstiel, R., *Detection Theory: Applications and Digital Signal Processing*, Boca Raton, FL: CRC Press, 2002.

[17] Ward, J., "Space-Time Adaptive Processing for Airborne Radar," Technical Report 1015, Lincoln Lab, MIT, 1994.

7

Cryptography Fundamentals

7.1 Introduction

7.1.1 Connection with Signals Collection

This chapter explains the primary issues with the internals part of signal collections. The earlier chapters discussed many aspects of fundamental signal collection, especially the estimation of the external parameters of a given signal. Such signal features include the center frequency and bandwidth of the radar waveform, as well as other basic signal properties of radar-pulse duration and pulse-repetition intervals. In addition, the modulation type is another primary signal external parameter.

The process of demodulation within the signal receiver yields a sequence of digital symbols. For example, the use of 8-PSK modulation/demodulation gives three bits for each of the $8 = 2^3$ possible phase symbols. A sequence of such 3-bit symbols is juxtaposed end-to-end to give a 1-D stream of bits, (i.e., zeros and ones). The interpretation of such a sequence of bits depends upon the signal type. Each class of signal is developed based upon an agreement of the meaning of the bits between the transmitter and the receiver. That is, groups of bits constitute various fields to be used in the communication process. Most signals include information regarding the identification of the sender and receiver, as well as other information and flags that specify the way the receiver is to process the entirety of the sequence of bits. In many cases, a portion of the bits have been encrypted to provide confidentiality over an open air, insecure medium to the destination receiver. The goal of the uncooperative intercept receiver is to process the input radar waveform to yield the modulated bitstream for cases in which the collected data corresponds to a communications waveform. Then, if a portion of the bitstream appears randomized, it may be useful to pass these encrypted bits to other algorithms that attempt to determine either the underlying stream of information bits, or the secret key parameters, or both.

7.1.2 Primary Goals of Cryptography

In order to encrypt bits within a received signal, it is important to examine the primary goals transforming original plaintext bits into an obscure set of encrypted bits designed to frustrate uncooperative receivers. These goals are *confidentiality*, *integrity*, *authentication*, and *nonrepudiation*. Of these three, encryption of a payload of data bits can be the last step in processing a stream of information bits prior to modulation of a physical waveform *confidentiality* over an insecure, open, and uncontrolled wireless environment. Again, it is often necessary for the sender to include information regarding the identification number of the transmitter, as well as that of the wireless receiver as unencrypted bits to facilitate the correct processing by the intended receiver. These unencrypted addresses of the intended sender and receiver may correspond to a single link within a long chain of links between an original sending station at one end, and a final receiving station at the other. In fact, the identification addresses of these endpoint stations can be encrypted as well, although the addresses amongst two adjacent wireless nodes are sent in the clear. In implementations of the Transport Control Protocol (TCP)/Internet Protocol (IP), it is typically necessary to send the media access control layer 2 addresses in the clear. The endpoint station addresses lie at the network layer 3 and are sent in the clear for some protocols and encrypted for others. Thus, decryption may be necessary to determine the endpoint stations involved in the communication, as well as the intended message between them.

A second primary goal of cryptography is that of *integrity*. It is necessary for the receiver to have high confidence that the underlying message has not been altered during transmission, even by a single bit. Hash functions and message integrity codes (MICs) are used to ensure the integrity of the underlying message. For some types of encryption, it is possible for an attacker to modify the contents of a message without decrypting it.

A third goal of cryptography is *authentication*. This covers the ability of the receiver to verify that the communication session is with the intended sender, and the ability of the sender to confirm that the session involves the intended receiver. In some applications, the actual message contents may be unencrypted, and yet cryptography methods are necessary for the receiver to have extremely high confidence that the message arrived from the intended sender.

A fourth goal is that of *nonrepudiation*, which is related to authentication. This prevents reply attacks, which have obvious implications in the financial realm. For example, suppose a person withdraws some amount of funds from a bank account, and then withdraws the same amount an hour later on the same day. The bank must then be able to prove to any third party that there were indeed two financial transactions rather than one.

7.1.3 Primary Algorithm Types

There are two primary types of cryptographic algorithms. The first is *symmetric key cryptography*. This methodology has been known and used for millennia and typically involves the use of a single shared key between the sender and the receiver. This methodology, in turn, can be implemented by two primary classes of cipher: stream and block. Stream ciphers operate independently on each individual bit of an input sequence of bits, typically through the application of a sequence of randomizing bits. In contrast, block ciphers operate on a finite set of input bits, usually a power of 2, and generate the same number of output bits. Of these two types, stream ciphers are typically easier to implement, whereas block ciphers typically offer greater security.

The second type is *asymmetric key cryptography*, in which one key is used by the sender and typically a different but related key for the receiver. Specifically, if the first key is used to encrypt a plaintext message into ciphertext prior to transmission over an insecure medium, then the second key is required for the receiver to decrypt the received ciphertext and extract the original plaintext message. Without this second key, the receiver is unable to perform the decryption process. This methodology is often referred to as *public key cryptography* because such asymmetric techniques often involve the specification that one of the keys is publicly available, and the other is a privately held by one user. These techniques are often used for message confidentiality, authentication, and to exchange symmetric keys for more intensive secure data transfer.

7.2 Mathematical Fundamentals of Cryptography

7.2.1 Modulo Arithmetic

The mathematical mechanics of cryptography is a large and complicated topic of which comprehensive coverage is well beyond the scope of this book. A full understanding of these concepts requires an understanding of abstract algebra topics including mathematical constructs referred to as groups, rings, integral domains, fields, and finite fields. For the practical implementation of cryptography applied to sequences of message bits on today's digital computers, the constructs of finite fields are most relevant. A finite field is defined for the operations of addition and multiplication, including that of the inverse for both operations. For implementation of finite field operations on digital computers, it is necessary to perform operations by using modulo arithmetic, which is discussed next.

The modulus is defined as follows. Suppose that the variable a is an integer and n is a positive integer. Then we define the value of a modulus n as the following:

$$a \bmod n = r \tag{7.1}$$

with the value of r is equal to the remainder after n is divided by a. That is, first compute the integer quotient q as defined via:

$$q = \left\lfloor \frac{a}{n} \right\rfloor \tag{7.2}$$

Here, the notation $\lfloor \cdot \rfloor$ denotes the greatest integer that is less than or equal to a/n, so that:

$$\left\lfloor \frac{a}{n} \right\rfloor \leq \frac{a}{n} < \left\lfloor \frac{a}{n} \right\rfloor + 1 \tag{7.3}$$

Then, the remainder r falls within the span:

$$0 \leq r < n \tag{7.4}$$

Also, the resulting integer quotient q and the remainder r satisfy:

$$a = qn + r \tag{7.5}$$

For example, to compute 62 mod 19, we first use the quotient $62/19 = 3.263158$ to calculate the integer quotient $q = \lfloor 62/19 \rfloor = 3$. Then, (7.5) implies that the remainder of the modulus operation is 5, as shown in Figure 7.1. For negative values of a and n, (7.1) to (7.5) are applied in the same manner, where the notation $\lfloor \cdot \rfloor$ denotes the greatest integer that is less than or equal to the applied argument. Figure 7.2 provides an example with a negative value of a.

$62 \bmod 19 = ?$

$62/19 = 3.263158$

$q = \lfloor 62/19 \rfloor = \lfloor 3.263158 \rfloor = 3$

$r = a - qn = 62 - \lfloor 62/19 \rfloor \times 19 = 62 - 3 \times 19 = 5$

$r = 62 \bmod 19 = 5$

Figure 7.1
First example of modulo operation.

$-62 \bmod 19 = ?$

$-62/19 = -3.263158$

$q = \lfloor -62/19 \rfloor = \lfloor -3.263158 \rfloor = -4$

$r = a - qn = -62 - \lfloor -62/19 \rfloor \times 19 = -62 - \{-4\} \times 19 = 14$

$r = -62 \bmod 19 = 14$

Figure 7.2
Second example of modulo operation, illustrating a case of a negative argument.

The essence of performing arithmetic modulo n is that it takes any one of the following values $\{0, 1, 2, \ldots, n-1\}$ as the input and maps to one of the same values as an output. Another property of modulo arithmetic is that the results are invariant to the order in which modulo computations of the form of (7.5) relative to that of the arithmetic operations are performed. For the first case, let us examine the operation of addition of any two integers a and b with modulo n. One possible means of performing the computation is to add a and b initially, following by the operation mod n. As an alternative method of performing this computation, it is possible to first compute a mod n and b mod n, followed by the addition of the result. However, the addition of a mod n and b mod n could yield a value that lies outside of the required span between 0 and $n-1$, so it is necessary to perform the mod n as a final step. The equivalence of these two methods for computing addition mod n is encapsulated via Figure 7.3. Similar equations apply for the operations of addition and subtraction, as are shown in this figure as well.

The use of integer exponents a^p under modulo operations is performed via repeated applications of the multiplication rule in Figure 7.3, involving a total of p factors of a. An example of this process is illustrated in Figure 7.4.

7.2.2 Euler's Totient Function

One of the most prominent asymmetric cryptographic methods is that of the RSA (Rivest-Shamir-Adleman) algorithm, which is a public key cryptosystem in four steps: key generation, key distribution, encryption, and decryption. One of the important functions that arises in the mechanics of the various operations in RSA is the computation of Euler's totient function. This function $\phi(n)$ is applied to a positive integer n, which is permitted to be either prime or nonprime. The totient function is defined to equal the number

$$\{a + b\} \bmod n = \{[a\ mod\ n] + [b\ mod\ n]\} \bmod n$$

$$\{a - b\} \bmod n = \{[a\ mod\ n] - [b\ mod\ n]\} \bmod n$$

$$\{a \times b\} \bmod n = \{[a\ mod\ n] \times [b\ mod\ n]\} \bmod n$$

Figure 7.3
Addition, subtraction, and multiplications under modulo operations.

$$13^{11} \bmod 17 = ?$$

$$13^2 \bmod 17 = \{13 \times 13\} \bmod 17 = 169 \bmod 17$$
$$= 169 - \lfloor 169/17 \rfloor \times 17 = 169 - 9 \times 17 = 16$$

$$13^4 \bmod 17 = \{13^2 \times 13^2\} \bmod 17 = \{16 \times 16\} \bmod 17 = 256 \bmod 17$$
$$= 256 - \lfloor 256/17 \rfloor \times 17 = 256 - 15 \times 17 = 1$$

$$13^8 \bmod 17 = \{13^4 \times 13^4\} \bmod 17 = \{1 \times 1\} \bmod 17 = 1$$

$$13^{11} \bmod 17 = \{13^8 \times 13^2 \times 13\} \bmod 17 = \{1 \times 16 \times 13\} \bmod 17$$
$$= 208 \bmod 17 = 208 - \lfloor 208/17 \rfloor \times 17 = 208 - 12 \times 17 = 4$$

Figure 7.4
The use of integer exponents under modulo operations is performed via repeated applications of the multiplication rule.

of positive integers that are less than n and are relatively prime to n. Two numbers are defined to be *relatively prime* if they share no common factors other than one. For example, the numbers 10 and 27 are relatively prime, since $10 = 2 \times 5$ and $27 = 3^3$ and thus have no common factors other than one.

As a first example, let us calculate Euler's totient function for a prime number p. For any such prime number p, every positive integer beginning with one and going up to $p - 1$, that is, $\{1, 2, 3, \ldots, p - 2, p - 1\}$, is relatively prime to p, since p is itself prime. Thus, $\phi(p) = p - 1$ for any prime number. For a second example, consider the product of two prime numbers (i.e., $n = pq$) with p and q equal to prime numbers. For this case, the value of Euler's totient function of the product of primes is equal to the product of Euler's totient function for each of the primes, that is, $\phi(n) = \phi(pq) = \phi(p)\phi(q) = \{p - 1\}\{q - 1\}$.

As a third example, Euler's totient function applied to a prime number p that is raised to some positive integral power, that is, yields $\phi(p^i) - \{p^i - p^{i-1}\}$. Number theory reveals the calculation of Euler's totient function generalizes in the following form for products of primes raised to positive integral powers: $\phi(p^i q^j \cdots r^k) = \{p^i - p^{i-1}\}\{q^j - q^{j-1}\} \cdots \{r^k - r^{k-1}\}$, for prime numbers $\{p, q, \cdots, r\}$ and positive integral powers $i, j, \cdots, k$. A summary of these Euler's totient function rules is shown in Figure 7.5.

Euler's totient function is essential in the definition of the primitive root of a positive integer n, which is used in some cryptographic

$$\phi(p) = p - 1$$
$$\phi(n) = \phi(pq) = \phi(p)\phi(q) = \{p - 1\}\{q - 1\}$$
$$\phi(p^i) = \{p^i - p^{i-1}\}$$
$$\phi(p^i q^j \cdots r^k) = \{p^i - p^{i-1}\}\{q^j - q^{j-1}\}\cdots\{r^k - r^{k-1}\}$$

prime numbers $\{p, q, \ldots, r\}$

positive integral powers $\{i, j, \cdots, k\}$

Figure 7.5
Summary of Euler's totient function rules.

processes, such as the Diffie-Hellman key exchange described later in this chapter. Consider a sequence of successive exponential powers of positive integer a from one up to $\phi(n)$, applied under modulo n, thus,

$$\left\{a, a^2, a^3, \ldots, a^{\phi(n)}\right\} \bmod n \tag{7.6}$$

Then, the integer a is a *primitive root* of the positive integer n if each of the exponential powers in (7.6) yields a distinct value under modulo n operations.

For example, determine if $a = 6$ is a primitive root of $n = 11$. Notice that $n = 11$ is prime, so that Euler's totient function is $\phi(11) = 10$. Then, the sequence of exponential powers of $a = 6$ up to $\phi(11) = 10$ gives:

$$\left\{6, 6^2, 6^3, 6^4, 6^5, 6^6, 6^7, 6^8, 6^9, 6^{10}\right\} \bmod 11 = \{6, 3, 7, 9, 10, 5, 8, 4, 2, 1\} \tag{7.7}$$

Thus, each element of the sequence yields a unique output value of the exponentiation under modulo arithmetic, so that $a = 6$ is indeed a primitive root of $n = 11$.

Next, determine if $a = 5$ is a primitive root of $n = 11$. Thus, the sequence of exponential powers up to $\phi(11) = 10$ yields:

$$\left\{5, 5^2, 5^3, 5^4, 5^5, 5^6, 5^7, 5^8, 5^9, 5^{10}\right\} \bmod 11 = \{5, 3, 4, 9, 1, 5, 3, 4, 9, 1\} \tag{7.8}$$

The elements of this sequence are not unique and instead repeat after every five elements. Therefore, that $a = 5$ is *not* a primitive root of $n = 11$.

7.3 Symmetric Cryptography

7.3.1 Model of Symmetric Cryptography

The essential model of symmetric cryptography is shown in the process diagram of Figure 1.1 in Chapter 1. The procedure begins with the distribution or generation of a key K that is shared by two users who need to send and receive information with one another. It is possible that these two users are communicating directly over a shared wireless or wired channel, where the concept of a wired channel encompasses a wide variety of physical media, including coaxial cables and fiber-optics. These two users can also be widely separated and connected over the span of many intervening links, which can be of different types, as with two users on the internet. The distribution of the shared key to the two users is often performed via asymmetric cryptography, which is the subject of the next subsection. Another possibility is for both users to send a public key to one another, from which a shared key is generated for each of the two users. Regardless of the approach, the result of the initial stage of symmetric cryptography is that each user is in possession of a shared key that is not available to anyone else.

The second step begins with a plaintext message M dataset, which is often encoded in a widely known format, as with common ASCII, document, and briefing file formats. This plaintext is entered into the sender's encryption algorithm, together with the shared symmetric key K, to yield the corresponding ciphertext C. This processing is described using the notation $E\{\cdot\}$ for the symmetric encryption process, with the arguments given by M and K:

$$C = E\{M, K\} \tag{7.9}$$

This ciphertext C is sent to the receiving station and appears to be an unintelligible random bit sequence to any unintended recipient who does not possess the key K that is shared between the intended users. This ciphertext may be required to traverse only a single point-to-point link, or it could also be the encrypted payload for a set of transport control segments that must traverse a sequence of data links in being routed from the sender to the receiver over a complex network (e.g., the internet).

The third and final step of symmetric cryptography is receipt of the ciphertext C at the receiving station. This ciphertext is entered into a decryption algorithm $D\{\cdot\}$ that effectively undoes all the permutations and mixing of the encryption algorithm $E\{\cdot\}$ by using the same shared key K that was applied at the sender's station to scramble the original plaintext message M. This symmetric decryption process is described using the following notation:

$$M = D\{C,K\} \tag{7.10}$$

7.3.2 Key Generation and Distribution

The application of symmetric cryptography requires the use of a key K that is shared by the sending and receiving stations. One methodology is to use a shared certification authority that provides this shared information amongst users who are required to communicate with one another. Another possibility is for the two stations to generate a shared key without the requirement for prior agreement pertaining to shared information. This section describes a basic straightforward mechanism based on the mathematical technique described earlier in this chapter, the Diffie-Hellman key exchange.

7.3.2.1 Diffie-Hellman Key Exchange

The Diffie-Hellman key exchange requires no prior information to be shared between the two users involved in the intended communication. Figure 7.6 presents the details involved in the generation of a key K that is then shared amongst two users. For this scenario, one user, Alice, initiates the generation of the shared key with an intended communication partner Bob. To begin this process, Alice selects a prime number p and a primitive root g of p such that $g < p$. In addition, Alice selects a private key α such that $\alpha < p$ and then computes the corresponding public key A via the computation $A = g^a \bmod p$.

Alice sends the values of the prime number p, the generator g, and the public key A over the insecure transmission medium to Bob.

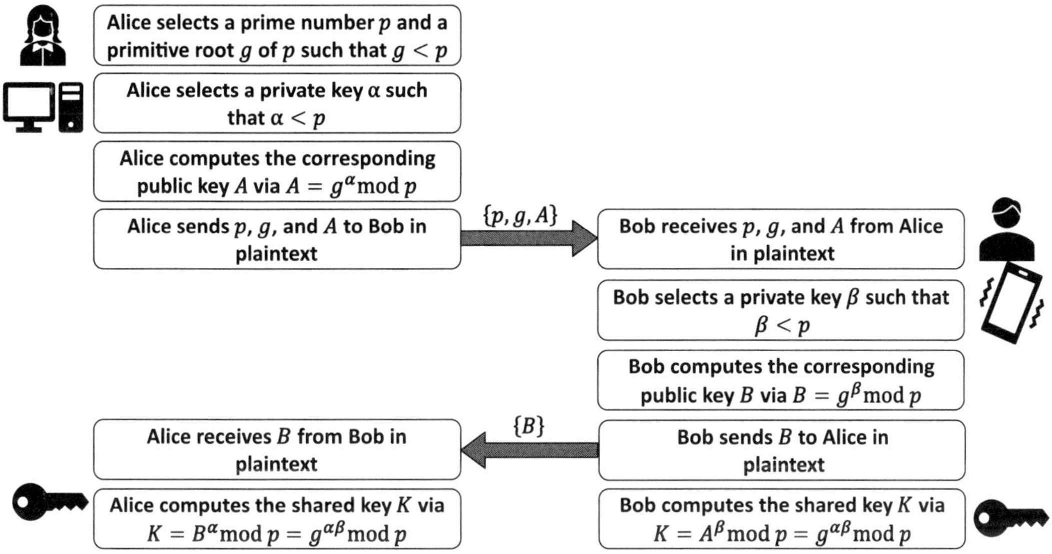

Figure 7.6
Diffie-Hellman key exchange for symmetric key cryptography.

Then, Bob selects a private key β such that $\beta < p$ and computes the corresponding public key B using $B = g^{\beta} \bmod p$. Next, Bob sends the public key B over the insecure medium to Alice. Upon receipt of Bob's public key B, Alice can compute the value of the common key K that is to be shared between them via $K = B^{\alpha} \bmod p = \{g^{\beta}\}^{\alpha} \bmod p = g^{\alpha\beta} \bmod p$, using the laws of powers of powers for modulo arithmetic that follow ordinary arithmetic. In tandem, Bob can compute the same shared common key K based upon Alice's public key A and his own private key β via $K = A^{\beta} \bmod p = \{g^{\alpha}\}^{\beta} \bmod p = g^{\alpha\beta} \bmod p$.

At this point in the Diffie-Hellman key exchange, both Alice and Bob share a common secret key K that has not been sent over the insecure medium. The security of this key exchange relies on the algorithmic difficulty in computing discrete logarithms efficiently. However, Diffie-Hellman methodology is vulnerable to the man-in-the-middle (MITM) class of cyber attacks. There exist more advanced and secure methodologies, such as the ElGamel and elliptic curve cryptosystems, but Diffie-Hellman offers a straightforward example that uses the mathematical concepts described earlier in this chapter.

For example, assume that Alice selects the prime number $p = 11$ and the primitive root $g = 6$ of $p = 11$, as was demonstrated in Section

7.2.2, which also satisfies $g < p$. Also, suppose that Alice selects the private key $\alpha = 7$, which satisfies $\alpha < p$. Then, Alice computes the corresponding public key A via $A = g^{\alpha} \bmod p = 6^7 \bmod 11 = 8$. Alice sends $\{p, g, A\} = \{11, 6, 8\}$ over the insecure transmission medium to Bob. Next, assume that Bob selects the private key $\beta = 3$, which satisfies $\beta < p$. Then, Bob computes the corresponding public key B using $B = 6^3 \bmod 11 = 7$ and sends it over the insecure medium to Alice. After receiving Bob's public key B, Alice computes the shared key K via $K = B^{\alpha} \bmod p = 7^7 \bmod 11 = 6$. Likewise, Bob computes the same shared key K by using Alice's public key $A = 8$ and his own private key $\beta = 3$ via $K = 8^3 \bmod 11 = 6$. Therefore, both Alice and Bob share the same common key of $K = 6$, which has not been sent over the insecure transmission medium.

7.3.3 Stream Ciphers

As discussed above, symmetric key cryptography is implemented by two classes of cipher: stream and block. Stream ciphers operate independently on each individual bit of an input sequence of bits, as can be implemented via a sequence of randomizing bits. In contrast, block ciphers operate on a finite set of input bits, usually a power of 2, which then produces the same number of output bits. This section presents the primary characteristics of both types of symmetric key cryptography.

7.3.3.1 Random Sequences

Stream ciphers rely upon the use of a random bitstream to generate a ciphertext bitstream that has no obvious pattern or structure. That is, the required ciphertext stream appears be a random sequence of zeros and ones, as could be generated by random flips of an unbiased coin to give a random sequence of heads versus tails. Physical systems appear to exist that can be used to give a truly random sequence of random bits. Examples include sources of entropy or randomness, including movements of a computer mouse or timing patterns of access on a computer disc [1]. However, cryptographic security requires that the randomizing bitstream never repeat during the time interval of the transmission of the bit packets, and it is difficult to extract a truly random bitstream of sufficient length for the secure transmission of large data sets. As such, it is often necessary for practical communications systems to generate deterministic bitstreams that mimic truly random bitstreams. This strategy can be sufficiently secure provided that the resulting pseudorandom bitstream never repeats over the transmission interval of the data packets.

There are methodologies for generating pseudorandom bitstreams. One algorithm is the Blum Blum Shub (BBS), which derives its names from its originators [1, 4]. Figure 7.7 shows the overall process diagram for the BBS generator, which begins with a random number seed. This seed s can be set equal to a shared secret key K, as described above, or it can be derived from such a key. First, the iterated variable x is set equal to the input seed value s. Second, this variable x is squared under the preselected modulo n, that is, $x^2 \bmod n$, and the resulting value is set equal to the new value of x. Next, the least significant bit of this new x is extracted to be the next bit within the generated pseudorandom bitstream. The computation of $x^2 \bmod n$ is again applied, but to the new x value. Then, the resulting value gives a yet newer value of x from which the least significant bit is extracted as the next bit in the pseudorandom bitstream. This process is applied repeatedly provided that additional pseudorandom bits are required.

As an example, assume that the operations are performed with $n = 101$, and the random number seed is selected to be $s = 18$. Then, the first 20 values of the sequence resulting from the computation of $x^2 \bmod n$ is shown in Figure 7.8. Examination of the resulting

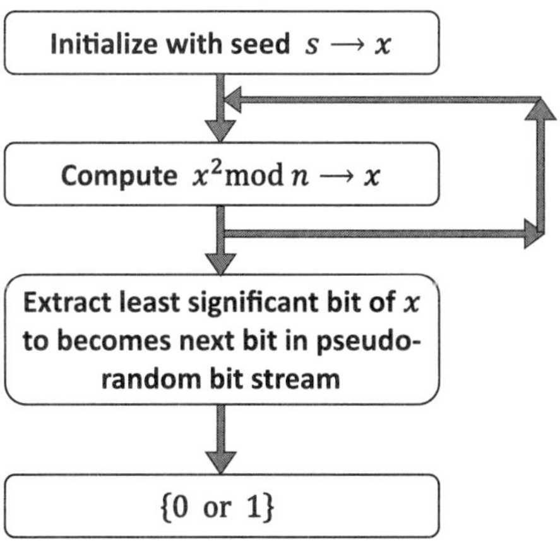

Figure 7.7
Blum Blum Shub generator of pseudorandom bitstreams.

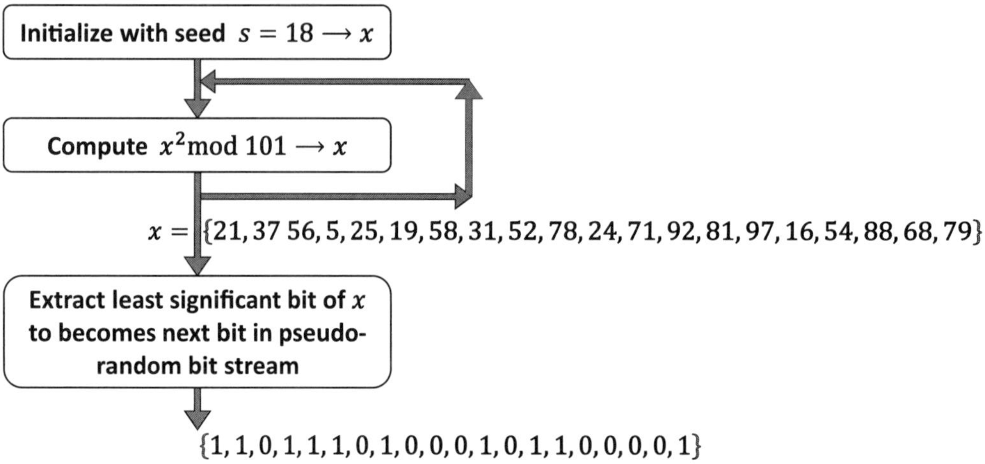

Figure 7.8
Example of using the Blum Blum Shub generator to give a pseudorandom bitstream.

bitstream reveals that 10-bit values are equal to zero and ten of them are ones, which is consistent with the expectation that any reasonable pseudorandom bitstream has approximately equal numbers of zeros and ones.

7.3.3.2 Stream Cipher Processing

Stream ciphers apply a random bitstream to transform an input plaintext bitstream to generate an obscure ciphertext bitstream for transmission across an insecure medium. Upon receipt at the receiving station, the same processing is applied to transform the received ciphertext bitstream back into the original plaintext bitstream. Often, simple exclusive-or (XOR) processing is applied for the bit-by-bit processing at both the sending and receiving stations. The symbol $\oplus$ is used to denote the XOR operator, and Figure 7.9 shows the matrix of outputs corresponding to the inputs. Thus, $0 \oplus 1 = 1$ and $1 \oplus 1 = 0$, and so on.

Figure 7.10 shows an example of using a pseudorandom bit sequence to encrypt an input plaintext bit sequence at the transmitting. This figure uses the sequence of 20-pseudorandom bits that are generated by the BBS generator of Figures 7.8. For each column in Figure 7.10, the XOR operator $\oplus$ is applied vertically to yield the result below the long horizontal line. This encryption process is

Exclusive Or (XOR)

⊕	0	1
0	0	1
1	1	0

Figure 7.9
Exclusive-or operator showing matrix outputs given the inputs.

applied at the transmitting station to yield a ciphertext bit sequence that can be sent over an insecure medium. At the receiver, this same pseudorandom bitstream is used to decrypt the input ciphertext into the original plaintext.

7.3.4 Block Ciphers

The previous section discussed the use of a stream cipher, which applies a sequence of pseudorandom bits—independently on each individual input bit—to encrypt a sequence of input plaintext bits. A stream cipher yields an output sequence of ciphertext bits at the sender, and performs the reverse decryption process at the receiver. In contrast, a block cipher operates on an entire group of plaintext bits as input to an encryption algorithm to produce a group of ciphertext bits of the same length, then performs the reverse for

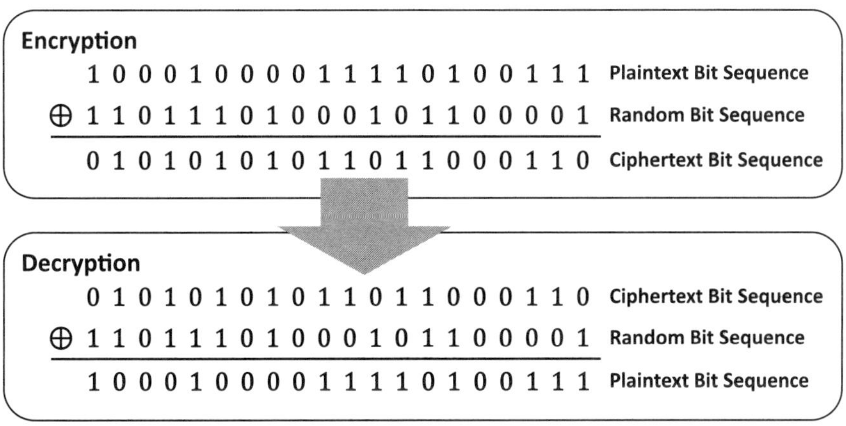

Figure 7.10
Use of a random bit sequence to perform encryption and decryption.

the decryption process. Figure 7.11 provides a graphical example of a notional simplified block cipher for two different key values. The left part of this figure transforms a block of 3-input plaintext bits into a block of 3-output ciphertext bits based upon a particular key value, with mapping lines traversing from left to right. The decryption process applies these same mapping lines but from right to left. The right part of this figure shows a notional transformation for a different key value, giving a significantly different mapping between the input plaintext bits and the output ciphertext bits.

Figures 7.9 and 7.10 highlight an important difference between stream and block ciphers. Consider the third input plaintext bit of a 0 within the plaintext of the upper part of Figure 7.10. Assume that this 0 is changed to a 1, so that the resulting third output ciphertext bit is also flipped from a 0 to a 1. However, all the other bit positions–both before and after–are unaltered. Thus, we arrive at an important property that is lacking in stream ciphers, which is that of diffusion. This useful security feature of a cryptographic algorithm requires that a flip in a single bit in an input set of bits resulting in the flipping of approximately one-half of all output bits. Consider the set of input plaintext bits corresponding to {0 1 0} in the right part of notional block cipher of Figure 7.11, which yields the output ciphertext {0 0 1}. Suppose that the third bit is flipped so that the input plaintext bits are {0 1 1}. Then, the resulting output ciphertext bit set is {1 1 1}, so that the flipping of the single bit

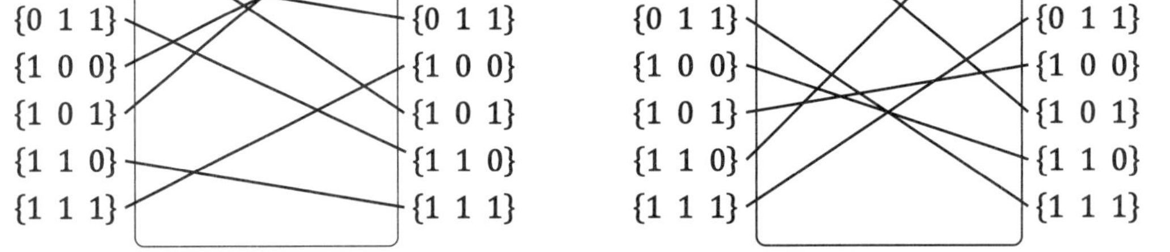

Figure 7.11
Simplified diagram of a notional simplified block cipher for two different key values.

in the third position yields a change in the two bits in both the first and second positions.

Block sizes for standard block encryption algorithms are typically equal to an exponential power of 2, and values of 128 and 256 are quite common. Thus, a well-designed block cipher algorithm will flip approximately one-half of the output bit values if only a single input bit is flipped. Another desirable quality of a well-designed block cipher is that the change of a single bit in the input key will give a flip of approximately one-half of the output bits, given the same set of input bits within the block. The significant difference in mappings of these two different notional keys in Figure 7.11 is the desired properties of a block cipher.

Many modern block encryption ciphers use the basic concepts of the Feistal algorithmic structure [1], which applies various processing steps of permutation and substitution over multiple rounds to ensure thorough diffusion. The Data Encryption Standard (DES) was established as an early block cipher in 1977 based upon the Feistal algorithmic structure. Various vulnerabilities that were later revealed led to the use of triple DES (3-DES) to enhance the security. The more secure block cipher Advanced Encryption Standard (AES) was established in 2001 and does not use the Feistal algorithmic structure directly, but does use its core principles of permutation and substitution applied over many rounds to give excellent diffusion properties. At the time of this writing, AES with a key size of 512 bits is the emerging ideal standard for symmetric cipher communication.

7.4 Asymmetric Cryptography

7.4.1 Basic Concepts

The sections above described the methods of symmetric cryptography, which uses only a single key K for sending an encrypted message across an insecure medium. In contrast, asymmetric cryptography relies upon the use of a pair of keys (see [2, 3]): (a) one of which is publicly available, and (b) the other held privately by a given user. The essential model of asymmetric cryptography for the purpose of confidentiality is given in the process diagram of Figure 7.12. This figure examines the case in which Alice intends to send a secure message to Bob. To do so, Alice must possess Bob's public key PU_{Bob}. It is assumed that there exists a methodology, such as a certificate authority, which is responsible for reliable distribution of the public keys required for asymmetric cryptography. The second key PR_{Bob} is held privately by Bob and is not available to anyone else, including Alice. Note that the notations PU_{Bob} and PR_{Bob} are used to denote the public and private keys, respectively, for asymmetric cryptography. In contrast, the notation K is used for shared key in symmetric cryptography.

After the distribution of the public keys, Alice encrypts the plaintext X dataset by using Bob's public key PU_{Bob} to give the corresponding ciphertext C. This processing is described using the notation $E\{\cdot\}$ for the asymmetric encryption process, with the arguments X and PU_{Bob}:

$$C = E\left\{X, PU_{\text{Bob}}\right\} \tag{7.11}$$

This ciphertext C is sent over the insecure medium, which can involve any number of discrete links within a complicated network. The next step of asymmetric cryptography involves receipt of the ciphertext C at the receiving station. This ciphertext is entered into an asymmetric decryption algorithm $D\{\cdot\}$ by using Bob's private key PR_{Bob}. This decryption process is described using the following notation:

$$X = D\left\{C, PR_{\text{Bob}}\right\} \tag{7.12}$$

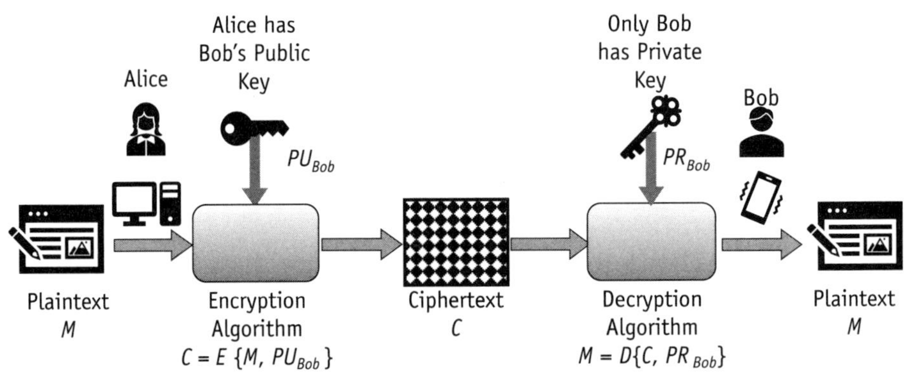

Figure 7.12
Asymmetric cryptography for message confidentiality.

Confidentiality is ensured, since only Bob is in possession of the private key PR_{Bob}.

It is also possible to apply these same concepts of asymmetric cryptography to ensure nonrepudiation by reversing the public and private keys of Figure 7.12, as shown in Figure 7.13. Here, Alice uses the private key PR_{Alice} to encrypt the plaintext message X to produce the ciphertext C via $C = E\{X, PR_{Alice}\}$, which is sent over the insecure media. Bob is in possession of Alice's public key PU_{Alice} and uses it to decrypt Alice's message to generate the plaintext X via $X = D\{C, PU_{Alice}\}$. In this scenario, Bob is assured that the message arrived from Alice—and nobody else—since only Alice is in possession of the corresponding private key PR_{Alice}. It is also possible to combine the methodologies of Figures 7.12 and 7.13 to ensure both confidentiality and nonrepudiation, although this requires the use of two sets of asymmetric key pairs.

7.4.2 RSA Algorithm

A common methodology used for implementing asymmetric cryptography in practice is based upon the RSA algorithm. RSA denotes the initials of the last names of the inventors: Ron Rivest, Adi Shamir, and Len Adleman at MIT [6]. Figure 7.13 presents the basic steps involved in generating the public and private keys for the RSA algorithm. First, the generator of the RSA keys must select prime numbers p and q such that $p \neq q$. Second, the product $n = pq$ is computed. Third, Euler's totient function is computed according

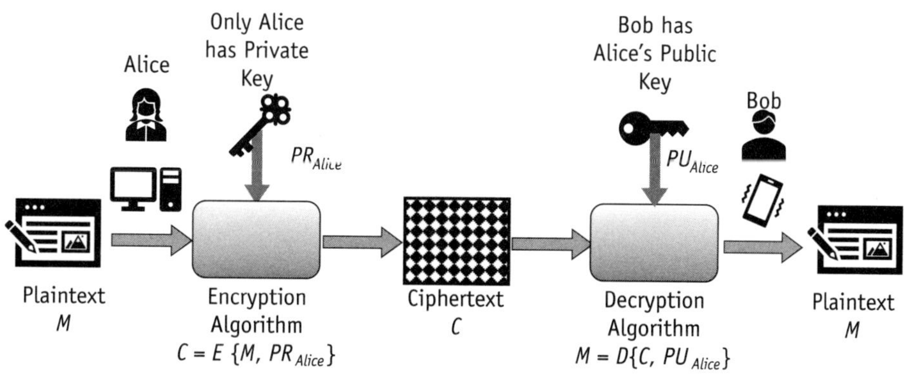

Figure 7.13
Asymmetric cryptography for message nonrepudiation.

to $\phi(n) = \phi(p)\phi(q) = \{p - 1\}\{q - 1\}$. Fourth, it is necessary to select an integer e that falls within the span $1 < e < \phi(n)$ and that has no common factors with $\phi(n)$ greater than one, that is, $gcd(e, \phi(n)) = 1$. Finally, the multiplicative inverse d is computed such that $d = e^{-1} \bmod \phi(n)$. This processing yields both the public key $\{n, e\}$ and the private key $\{n, d\}$.

Consider again the use of asymmetric cryptography for confidentiality by encrypting a message sent from Alice to Bob. The public and private keys of Figure 7.14 are used in Figure 7.15 to give the mathematical steps involved in the encryption and decryption process. For this scenario, Alice selects a plaintext message M that is to be encrypted for confidentiality. Then, Alice uses Bob's public key $PU_{\text{Bob}} = \{n, e\}$ to encrypt M via $C = E\{M, PU_{\text{Bob}}\} = M^e \bmod n$. This ciphertext C is sent over the insecure media. Upon receipt of this ciphertext, Bob uses the private key $PR_{\text{Bob}} = \{n, d\}$ to decrypt C via $M = D\{C, PR_{\text{Bob}}\} = C^d \bmod n$, thus yielding the original plaintext message M.

Consider the nonrepudiation scenario of Figure 7.14. Here, the RSA public and private keys are applied differently. Specifically, Alice selects a plaintext message M to be signed for nonrepudiation. Then, Alice uses private key $PR_{\text{Alice}} = \{n, d\}$ to encrypt M via $C = E\{M, PR_{\text{Alice}}\} = M^d \bmod n$. This encrypted message C is sent over the insecure media. After receiving this ciphertext, Bob uses Alice's public key $PU_{\text{Alice}} = \{n, e\}$ to decrypt C via $M = D\{C, PU_{\text{Alice}}\} =$

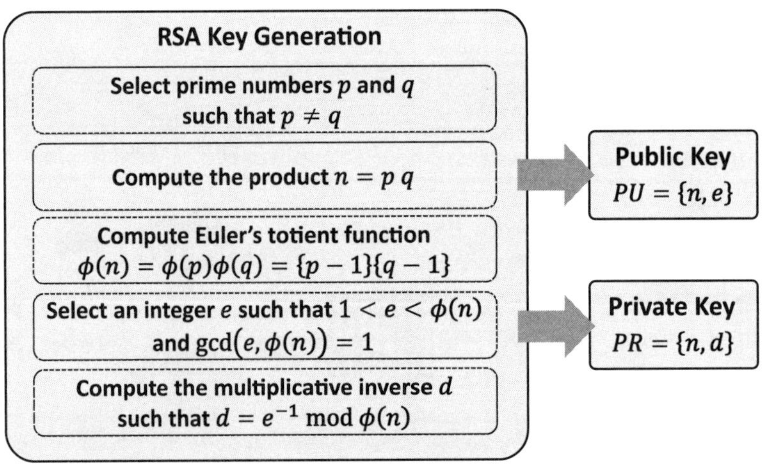

Figure 7.14
Generation of public and private keys in the RSA algorithm.

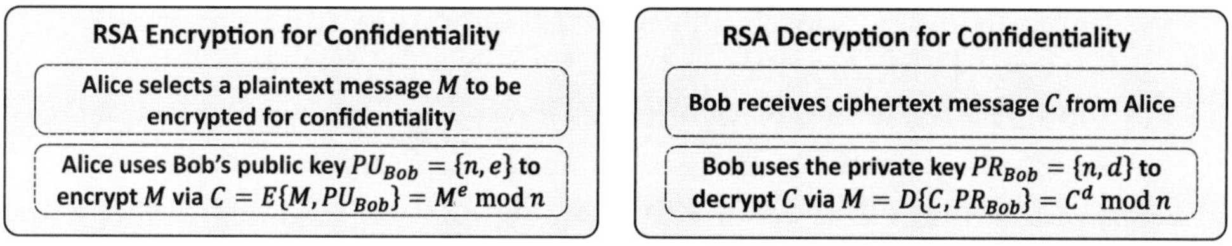

Figure 7.15
Use of RSA public and private keys for confidentiality, per the scenario of Figure 7.13.

$C^e \bmod n$, thus recovering the original message M. Again, only Alice could have sent this message by holding the private key, thereby providing the required nonrepudiation.

Next, we present an example of the RSA algorithm and the details of its processing, following Figure 7.14. First, we select the two distinct prime numbers $p = 5$ and $q = 11$, so that the product $n = 5 \times 11 = 55$ is computed as the second step. Third, Euler's totient function is computed via $\phi(55) = \phi(5)\phi(11) = \{5 - 1\}\{11 - 1\} = 40$. Fourth, we select an integer $e = 37$ that falls within the span $1 < e = 37 < \phi(55) = 40$ and that has no common factors with $\phi(55) = 40$ greater than one, that is, $gcd(37, 40) = 1$. The final step is the computation of the multiplicative inverse $d = e^{-1} \bmod \phi(n) = 37^{-1} \bmod 40 = 13$, which can be verified via $\{37 \times 13\} \bmod 40 = 481 \bmod 40 = 1$. This process generates both the RSA public key $\{n = 55, e = 37\}$ and the private key $\{n = 55, d = 13\}$.

The corresponding encryption and decryption are based upon these keys. First assume that we follow Figure 7.15 for confidentiality to encrypt a message $M = 52$. The corresponding ciphertext is computed using the RSA public key $\{n = 55, e = 37\}$. Then, Figure 7.15 implies $C = E\{M, PU_{\text{Bob}}\} = M^e \bmod n = 52^{37} \bmod 55$. We begin with $52^4 \bmod 55 = 26$. The rules of modulo arithmetic shown in Figure 7.4 reveal that $52^{16} \bmod 55 = 26^4 \bmod 55 = 36$, and in turn $52^{32} \bmod 55 = 36^2 \bmod 55 = 31$. Finally, the ciphertext is computed using $C = 52^{37} \bmod 55 = \{52^{32} \times 52^4 \times 52\} \bmod 55 = \{31 \times 26 \times 52\} \bmod 55 = 2$. That is, this ciphertext $C = 2$ is the encrypted message that is sent over the insecure channel.

The receiver obtains the ciphertext $C = 2$ from the encrypted communication and applies the rules of Figure 7.13 to determine the message based upon possession of the RSA private key $\{n = 55, d = 13\}$. Figure 7.13 specifies the computation of the original plaintext message via $M = D\{C, PR_{\text{Bob}}\} = C^d \bmod n = 2^{13} \bmod 55$. The result is found using $2^6 \bmod 55 = 9$, so that the modulo arithmetic rules in Figure 7.4 give $M = 2^{13} \bmod 55 = \{2^6 \times 2^6 \times 2\} \bmod 55 = \{9 \times 9 \times 2\} \bmod 55 = 52$, which is identical to the original plaintext $M = 52$. A similar approach can be used to apply RSA public and private keys for nonrepudiation, as shown in Figure 7.16.

7.5 Summary

This chapter summarized the essential concepts involved in cryptography of messages, which forms an important component of the internals of signals. The process for the collection and demodulation of signals from an emitter yields a sequence of symbols from which a bitstream can be extracted. The entirety or portions of this bitstream can be encrypted for various reasons, including attempts to ensure the confidentiality, integrity, authentication, and nonrepudiation of the subject message. Most cryptography is based upon the use of modulo arithmetic, due to the suitability of the corresponding discrete operations over a finite discrete set. In addition, this chapter introduced the concept of Euler's totient function, which is invoked in some of the basic cryptographic functions, including the RSA algorithm.

Next, the concepts of symmetric key cryptography were introduced, beginning with a discussion of symmetric key generation via the Diffie-Hellman key exchange. The details of a stream cipher were discussed, including an example of the BBS pseudorandom number generator. In addition, the basic concepts of block ciphers and the corresponding benefits of diffusions were explained. Finally, this chapter described the concepts of asymmetric cryptography, with a special emphasis on the RSA algorithm.

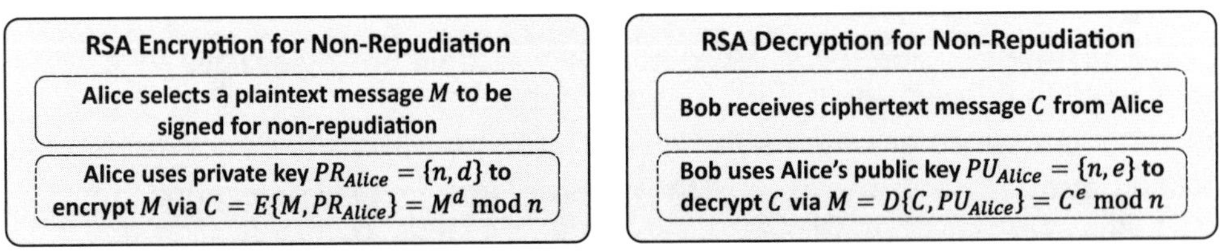

Figure 7.16

Use of RSA public and private keys for nonrepudiation, per the scenario of Figure 7.14.

This chapter focused upon the generation of cryptographic operations to ensure the confidentiality, integrity, authentication, and nonrepudiation of the messages that are transmitted over an insecure medium. The details for defeating these methods often exploits weaknesses in either the cryptographic algorithm itself, the length of the key, or in its implementation via a particular protocol. In addition, it is useful for the cryptanalyst, who is attempting to break the cryptographic operations, to obtain samples of plaintext-ciphertext pairs of messages sent over the insecure media. Thus, to have a robust cryptographic implementation, a cryptanalyst must use brute force techniques. If such brute force methods are all that are available to the cryptanalyst, then all possible key sequences and input plaintext sequences are equally likely. That is, a cryptanalyst would be required to test approximately one-half of all the possible key and plaintext sequences, on average, to break the algorithm. Significantly fewer numbers are required if the cryptanalyst discovers a flaw in the protocol or the underlying cryptographic function used to encrypt the data.

References

[1] Stallings, W., *Cryptography and Network Security: Principles and Practice*, 8th Edition, Hoboken, NJ: Pearson, 2020.

[2] Wu, Chwan-Hwa J., and Irwin, J. D., *Introduction to Computer Networks and Cybersecurity*, Boca Raton, FL: CRC Press, 2013.

[3] Chandra, P., *Bulletproof Wireless Security: GSM, UMTS, 802.11, and Ad Hoc Security*, Burlington, MA: Elsevier, 2005.

[4] Blum, L., Blum, M., and Shub, M., "A Simple Unpredictable Pseudo-Random Number Generator," *SIAM Journal on Computing*, No. 2, 1986.

[5] Stallings, W., *Data and Computer Communications*, Tenth Edition, Upper Saddle River, NJ: Pearson, 2014.

[6] Rivest, R., Shamir, A., and Adleman, L., "A Method of Obtaining Digital Signatures and Public Key Cryptosystems," *Communications of the ACM*, February 1978.

8

Signal Networks

8.1 Introduction

Much of the exposition from previous chapters included details on the emission, reception, processing, and exploitation of RF signals in the environment, often a signal transmitted by a particular node within a signal network. In general, such a network is comprised of many interconnected nodes, which can be connected in the form of a simple or complicated topology with encryption methods [1, 2]. General networks can be comprised of a variety of heterogeneous links connecting individual nodes.

8.1.1 Wired Signals

Various types of physical connections can exist between any two nodes. First, there are the *wired* connections, which are based upon the flow of electrons along metallic conductors (e.g., copper coaxial cables) or the flow of light, as within fiber optic cables. For these types of wired connections, almost all electromagnetic field energy is contained within 1-D lines of communication, with little or no field energy outside of these narrow channels of propagation. Wired connections also include the flow of electrons along metallic strip lines atop dielectric substrates, as within computer processing chips. For these wired connections, the EM field energy lies within the primary propagation channels of the conducting strips and dielectric substrates, although smaller amounts of EM energy can propagate outside of these materials.

8.1.2 Wireless Signals

The other primary type of physical connection between two nodes is the propagation of EM field energy from a transmitting antenna at one node, to a receiving antenna at a second node. For these *wireless* connections between a given pair of nodes, the EM field energy is not contained within a narrow 1-D channel, as typically occurs for wired connections [3]. Thus, the interception of wireless signals is easier and can be so frequent as to cause cochannel interference with other desired RF signals. As discussed in Chapter 4 on radar fundamentals, the transmission antenna has a physical gain power pattern, which has multiple lobes for maximum number of directions for EM propagation, as well as nulls where little or no EM energy is directed. Thus, the interception of such wireless signals can be straightforward, assuming that a radar receiver with sensitivity in the transmitted frequency band is placed in the direction of one of the primary lobes. This receiver antenna must be placed at a distance from the transmitter so that the received signal power lies sufficiently above the noise floor to enable target detection and exploitation accounting for the $1/R^2$ propagation loss, with R equal to the distance between the transmitter and the receiver. Wireless signals are explored in greater detail here, due to their prevalence and relative ease of interception.

8.2 Protocol Stack

The implementation of the data packets within wireless networks is typically based upon a stack of discrete layers. The network theory applies the International Standards Operation (ISO) model, which defines seven layers. However, practical issues led to the implementation of a five-layer model wherein the top three layers of the ISO model are combined into one layer. The final realization of the resulting 5-layer Internet Protocol stack is shown in Figure 8.1.

The initial description of the five protocol layers is described in a bottom-up formulation, beginning with the physical layer 1, the data link layer 2, the network layer 3, the transport layer 4, and the application layer 5. At the lowest level, the transmission of information occurs at the physical layer 1. Here, the concern is the ability to

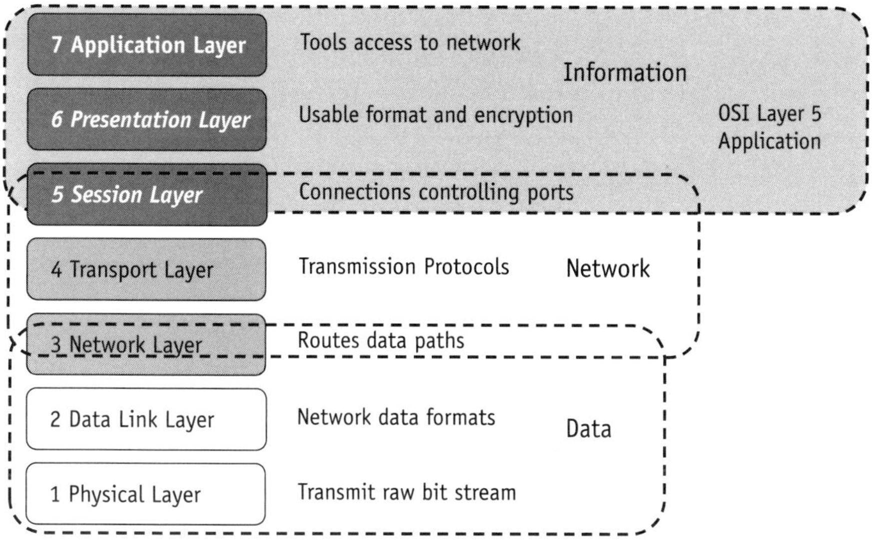

Figure 8.1
The seven layers of the Internet Protocol stack.

transmit a single symbol from one node to another adjoining node. As described above, the physical medium can be either wireless or wired, where the concept of wired includes fiber optic transmission as well as electrically conducting media.

8.2.1 Physical Layer

There are various modulation techniques that can be applied at the physical layer. First, AM methods can be applied, where the amplitude is changed to different discrete values to transmit correspondingly differing symbols. For example, assume that eight different amplitude levels are transmitted at one node, and then received and processed at an adjoining node. The transmission of one of these amplitude symbols conveys three bits of information, since $2^3 = 8$. This methodology is a type of amplitude shift keying. The most basic type of ASK is on-off modulation, where the signal is either present (i.e., it is on) or is absent (i.e., off). Such on-off ASK is used frequently in fiber optic links.

It is also possible to transmit information between two adjoining nodes by using FM, as in frequency shift keying, where one of several different frequencies is transmitted between the two nodes. It is possible to modulate information symbols between two adjoining nodes using phase-based modulation, as with phase shift keying.

It is also possible to combine the foundations of ASK, FSK, and PSK to yield more complicated modulation strategies. For example, quadrature amplitude modulation (QAM) is a combination of amplitude and phase modulation. In sending information over a physical medium between adjoining nodes, there must be an initial setup involving agreement between the two nodes, so that the receiving node is able to demodulate the symbols that were sent by the transmitter.

8.2.2 Data Link Layer

The second layer from the bottom of the Internet Protocol stack in Figure 8.1 is the data link layer, referred to as layer 2. This layer sends a group of bits between two adjoining nodes within a larger network. This group of bits is referred to as a *frame*. A typical data link layer frame involves a header, a trailer, and a payload, as shown in Figure 8.2.

The *data link header* contains required addressing information to ensure that the information is being sent from the correct transmitting station and is being received by the correct receiving station. This information is necessary since the physical medium connecting the adjoining nodes is often shared. For example, the internet architecture of a local area network (LAN) can involve a bus that connects several nodes on a shared electrically conducting line. Thus,

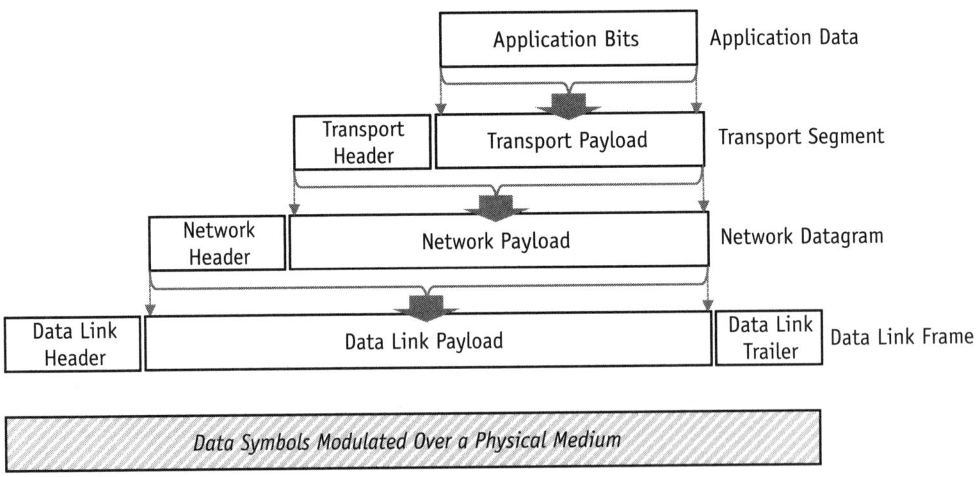

Figure 8.2
Encapsulation of payload layers in the Internet Protocol stack.

multiple receiving stations could demodulate a signal that was transmitted on the bus, but the message might be intended for only a single receiving station on the bus. That is, an unintended recipient would demodulate the signal and inspect the heading receiver address. If this receiver address within the data link layer does not match that of the receiving station itself, then this station simply discards this frame and stops processing it. However, if the receiver address within the data link frame matches that of the receiving station, or if this receiver address is the broadcast address, then this node retains the message and continues processing it as described in more detail below.

Although shared bus architectures comprise common architectures in wired media, the concept of a shared medium is even more prevalent in wireless networks. The EM energy in wireless networks in not confined to a narrow 1-D channel and instead can be intercepted by a multitude of receivers, provided that these antenna phase centers lie in physical directions corresponding to the beampattern of the transmitting antenna. Multiple wireless receivers can receive a given transmitted signal, and each receiver in the network must inspect the receiver address in the data link header to determine if this node is an intended receiver station. It is possible for an unintended receiver station to further process the frame even if it is not a recipient specified by the transmitting station.

The data link header also contains information about which *protocol* is to be invoked at the next higher layer in the protocol stack. For example, there are multiple protocols at network layer 3. However, the most common protocol at this network layer is called the *Internet Protocol*. Thus, one of the fields of the data link header contains the required protocol processing at the next layer, which again is commonly IP. In addition, the data link header contains information about throttling the flow of information from the transmitting station to the receiving station. This can be especially important if the receiving station is overwhelmed with the data flow, as when receiving too much data from other stations.

The next major part of the data link frame is the *payload*, which contains the information to be processed by the next layer up the Internet Protocol stack. If the data link header specifies that the next layer processing is to use the IP protocol, then this payload of the data link frame is passed up to the next layer of processing (i.e., network layer 3).

Link layer technology often includes a *trailer*, as shown in Figure 8.2. This trailer provides error detection, which performs a bitwise computation on the entire frame to determine if there have been any likely bit errors in the transmission-reception process. Such errors occur more frequently if the signal-to-interference plus noise drops to levels that are relatively too low, so that deleterious demodulation errors occur in the receiver station. One commonly used error-detection methodology is the cycle redundancy check (CRC) processing, used in 802.11 networks [3]. The CRC detects errors but does not have a provision for automatically correcting them. Typically, if the CRC processing detects a likely bit error in the data link frame, then messaging at layer 2 is used to notify the sending station to retransmit this frame. If layer 2 messaging is not available within a data link between two adjoining nodes, then it is necessary for higher layers in the Internet Protocol stack (of Figure 8.1) to detect that required information bits did not arrive at the receiving station as expected, and retransmission is needed.

8.2.3 Network Layer

The third layer beginning from the bottom of the protocol stack of Figure 8.1 is the network layer, or layer 3. Network layer technology involves the data necessary to send a packet from one node to another node over an entire network. Thus, an addressing mechanism is needed to specify the sending node and the final receiving node on the network.

The most common network layer protocol is the Internet Protocol, which is often abbreviated as IP. One version that is still used frequently is the fourth version IPv4, in which a given sending or receiving node is specified using four octets. The first octet is comprised of exactly eight bits, yielding a value between 0 and 255, inclusive. Likewise, each of the other three octets is specified as a number between 0 and 255. In total, a full IPv4 is expressed in a dotted decimal as four numbers, each with a value between 0 and 255, and in which the four numbers are separated by three dots or periods. Therefore, a sending node is specified using 32 bits in the IP format, and the same applies for the address of the receiving node.

A downside of the IPv4 approach is that the over 20 billion devices connected to the internet yields an insufficient number of network addresses to specify each node uniquely. Two workarounds that have been implemented for IPv4 are Classless Internet Domain Routing (CIDR) and Network Address Translation (NAT), which have been practical methods for accommodating the growing number of users on the internet. CIDR enables a given organization to allocate a number of bits that do not lie on the octet boundary, so that 9 or 13, and so on bits could be allocated, rather than only 8, 16, or 24. NAT allows a single IPv4 address to accommodate a large number of users behind the border router for an organization by using layer 4 addressing, which is discussed in the next subsection. In addition, IPv6 is used much more frequently and will be able to accommodate the number of nodes for many years.

8.2.4 Transport Layer

The fourth layer from the bottom of the protocol stack of Figure 8.1 is the transport layer, which is often referred to as layer 4. The transport layer is responsible for providing a port or service number in support of applications. The use of different port numbers on a given device enables communications with multiple separate applications to run simultaneously. Therefore, port numbers facilitate interprocess communication between two users on the network, so that, with the exception of various delays in sending packets from one node to another, the process activities seem to occur seamlessly between the two nodes.

For example, suppose that a given user opens two different browsers on a single computer. Also assume that a user performs a search for tennis rackets in the first browser and dog food for the second browser. As part of the hypertext protocol request, such as HTML (HyperText Markup Language), separate port numbers are assigned by the operating system to the two different browser windows. The transport layer addressing scheme facilitates interprocess communication where the separate port numbers are attached to HyperText Transport Protocol (HTTP) request messages that could potentially be sent to the same server at a potentially remote location. The server will use these same port numbers to send separate responses that are intended to be processed separately by the two different browsers. Thus, when each communication packet is received by the computer, the operating system determines the appropriate browser that is to receive that message, and then sends the message to this application. In this way, the port addressing scheme described above enables multiple applications to communicate with the open internet simultaneously.

The transport layer addressing is also important in another concept mentioned earlier, NAT. The port addressing capabilities on a network permit a single externally facing IP address to support many users within a LAN. The transport layer methodology functions as follows: consider a subnet that must support multiple users with only a single externally facing IPv4 address. The subnet strategy works if there are multiple separate internal IP addresses that are assigned within the subnet. These internal IP addresses are not available to the outside internet. Suppose that one of these internal users wants to send a HTTP request to a server on the open internet. Then, the border gateway router for the subnet containing the first user assigns a different port number for the outgoing packet and makes all appropriate modifications to the packet. This border gateway router also maintains a mapping between the internal IP address and port number pair, which is called a socket, and the outgoing and externally facing IP address and port number pair. Thus, any return packets from the server will have this same externally facing IP address and port number pair as destination addresses for layers 3 and 4. The border gateway router then translates and thus modifies the IP address and port number within this packet so that it is routed to the intended application of the original user within the subnet. The border gateway router can support many users via NAT by using different external port numbers for different users, although the external IP addresses for all supported users is the same. The external port number provides the border gateway router with a mechanism for tracking communication with various users within its subnet.

Two common protocols at layer 4 are User Datagram Protocol (UDP) and Transport Control Protocol (TCP). The simpler protocol of the two is UDP, since it provides only a *best effort* type of transmission of segments at layer 4. The format of a UDP packet is presented in Figure 8.3 and includes the following: (a) 16 bits for the source port number, (b) 16 bits for the destination port number, (c) 16 bits to delineate the total length of the segment, (d) 16 bits of checksum to provide for an error-detection capability, and (e) the payload bits of the application being supported at layer 5.

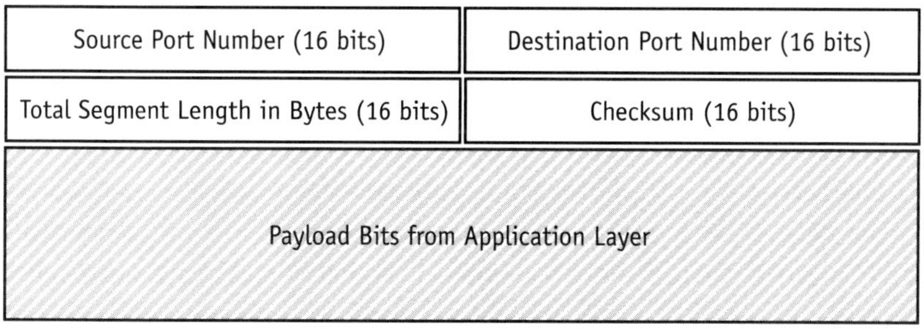

Figure 8.3
The format of the UDP packet.

Thus, the UDP protocol is relatively lightweight in terms of fields within the layer 4 format and its corresponding functionality. In particular, UDP does not possess the ability to provide flow control, acknowledgment of the receipt of each byte within the payload, and other additional services. UDP supports *connectionless* communications services where packets are sent independently of one another, without being explicitly associated with one another in a stream of messages.

One application that utilizes the services of UDP is that of domain name services (DNS), which is a distributed database that converts commonly used uniform resource locator (URL) names into the IP addresses required at layer 3. As a connectionless protocol, UDP packets are sent to make inquiries without the need to initiate a session, and later terminate it as part of making such DNS inquiries. The strategy of DNS is that in the event of no reply to an inquiry, another inquiry is repeated after the expected round trip of the first message has expired. A requirement to initiate and later terminate transport layer sessions would only give additional undesired delays due to the round-trip propagation times.

There exist many communications needs for which the connectionless, best-effort services of UDP are insufficient. For example, consider the transmission of application data from one location to another in a network. For some applications, the quantity of data to be sent can be relatively large. Also, the flipping of a single bit might cause the application to malfunction. Thus, it is important to have a layer 4 protocol that provides for the reliable transmission of all bits of a large application data packet without error. TCP provides such connection-oriented transmission services at layer 4. TCP, along with the IP, provides the common terminology of the TCP/IP protocol suite to support the enterprise networks of the internet. The structure of the fields of TCP is illustrated in Figure 8.4.

The format of a TCP segment includes the following: (a) 16 bits for the source port number, (b) 16 bits for the destination port number, (c) 32 bits to delineate the specific bytes of the application data that have been sent from the source node for the given transport layer segment, (d) 32 bits to delineate the specific bytes of the application data that have been received at the destination node for the given segment, (e) 16 bits of various flags to delineate specific functional packets within a transport stream, (f) 16 bits of receive window size to specify the maximum amount of data that the source is allotted to send to the receiver, (g) 16 bits of checksum to provide for an error-detection capability, (h) 16 bits to specify a potential urgent data capability, (i) a variable number of option bits, and (j) the payload bits of the application being supported at layer 5. These various fields are needed to support the reliable transport of a large application-layer data packets by breaking the original package of bits into smaller transport layer segments, which are reassembled

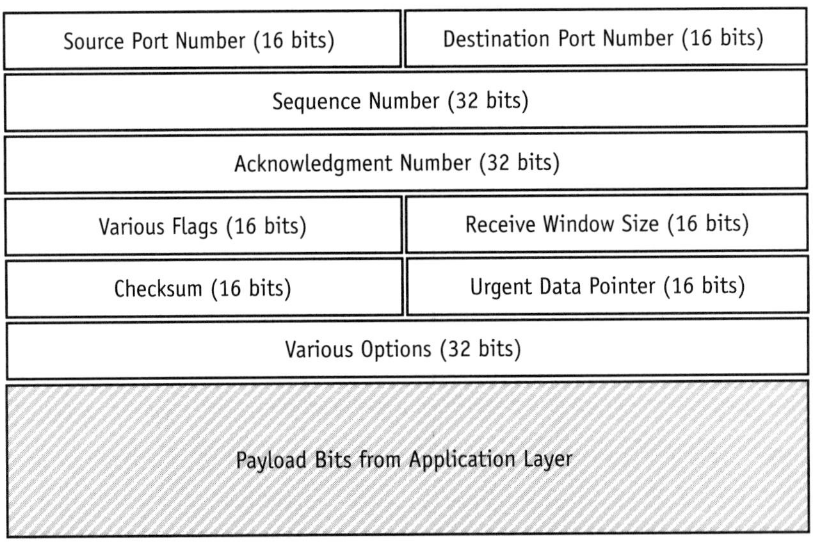

Figure 8.4
The format of the TCP packet.

and properly ordered to assimilate the desired message data at the destination node.

8.2.5 Application Layer

The fifth layer from the bottom of the protocol stack in Figure 8.1 is the application layer, also known as layer 5. The application layer supports the use of programs that typical users interact with. A primary goal of signal networks is to provide interprocess communication to enable seamless interaction between users on different parts of the global network. Examples include HTTP, FTP, and Simple Mail Transfer Protocol (SMTP).

One of the most common applications is for web browsers. The supporting set of rules for this interaction is HTTP. In a typical interaction, a user enters a URL into the browser, which results in a *HTTP GET* message being sent from the client machine to the server. A packet must be generated containing the contents of this HTTP GET request as a payload for transport layer segments. A given transport segment is then the payload for a network layer datagram, which in turn is a payload for a data link layer frame, as shown in Figure 8.2. Therefore, frames containing the HTTP GET data often traverse multiple links in a heterogeneous network in being routed to the destination server.

The server receives this HTTP GET message and generates an appropriate response, which is often sent as a HTTP 200 OK message containing the desired data. This HTTP message is encapsulated within the various layers of the TCP/IP protocol stack, which yields a response back to the client after traversing multiple links in a heterogeneous network. For a normally functioning network with typical subsecond total delays, the interprocess communication between the client and server functions seamlessly across the global TCP/IP network, just as if all machines were located in the same room.

8.3 Types of Message Delay

The current section examines issues in the delay between the time that a message is sent from a given station at one location, and when it is received at the destination station at another location. The goal is to minimize delay, so that the application communications across the global internet have the feel of occurring locally within a single computer system. However, the implementation of datagram packet delivery across the complex global network of heterogeneous data links implies that multiple significant contributions to packet delay exist, including propagation delay, transmission delay, router processing delay, and queuing delay. Each of these elements are discussed, together with implications for signals detection and characterization.

8.3.1 Propagation Delay

One primary contribution to delay in networks is propagation delay. Consider the modulation of a message at the sender station (e.g., point A) and the resulting demodulation at the destination (e.g., point B). For the sake of argument, initially consider just a single bit within this message. The overall propagation delay time t_{prop} required for this single bit to travel from point A to point B is equal to the total distance D of traversal between point A and point B along the relevant lines-of-communication divided by the average speed of travel, often modeled to be $s \cong 2 \times 10^8$ meters per second based upon the typical speed of light in fiber. Thus, the propagation delay is often modeled to be: $t_{prop} = D/s$.

If a particular bit travels over a distance of D = 200 km, then the corresponding propagation delay is $t_{prop} = D/s = 1$ millisecond. However, consider a case in which the data packet travels in an eastward direction over a distance of D_1 = 200 km to arrive at a particular router, which then sends the packet in a southward direction for an additional D_2 = 100 km. Then, the propagation delay for any given bit within this packet is equal to $t_{prop} = \{D_1 + D_2\}/s = 1.5$ milliseconds.

A related time-of-interest is the *roundtrip time* (RTT) for a given message to traverse the distance from the sender station (e.g., point A) to a particular destination (e.g., point B), followed by the traversal of the response message from point B back to point A. Thus, an estimate of the roundtrip time between points A and B within a network is equal to twice the one-way propagation delay between the two points. Both routers and end users within a network typically compute estimates of the roundtrip times involved in sending messages between two given points to optimize communications performance. For example, applications operating at layer 5 in the standard TCP/IP protocol stack typically apply sequences of messages for a given transaction, often involving queries or requests followed by responses. Consider a situation in which a given client station at point A attempts to send a message that is intended to arrive at a given server station at point B. Assume that this message is lost due to a communications failure along a particular data link operating at layer 2 in the TCP/IP protocol stack. If the two stations have exchanged messages within a given TCP session, then the sending station at point A has generated an estimate of the RTT. The RTT gives a duration for the total time interval that the sending station should wait before concluding that the original message was lost or dropped, thus requiring retransmission of the message.

Typically, Kalman filtering is applied to generate estimates of the roundtrip time by combining the measurements of D/s corresponding to recent messages, with older values of D/s to smooth or average out large deviations in delay due to changing network conditions. If the resulting estimates of the roundtrip time is too large, then the sending station waits too long before retransmitting, thereby delaying the overall receipt of the intended message. If the roundtrip time estimates are too small, then the sending station could send a duplicate message before the receiving station's response message is received. In this scenario, multiple duplicate request messages are congesting the network, thereby degrading overall network performance.

8.3.2 Transmission Delay

The previous section discussed the delay in sending a given bit of a message over a distance. However, the messages sent in datagram networks include many bits for a given datagram, and a sending station is not able to transmit all of these bits instantaneously. Instead, a nonzero finite time is required for all bits within a given datagram to be transmitted out of the network interface controller of that station. This *transmission delay* t_{trans} is equal to the ratio of the message length L in bits divided by the transmission rate R (i.e., $t_{\text{trans}} = L/R$). Basically, the transmission delay is the time required to modulate or transmit all of the symbols of a message comprised of L bits.

For example, consider a scenario where two adjacent nodes on a network are connected by a data link with a maximum transmission rate between the two nodes equal to $R = 10$ Gbps $= 10^{10}$ bits per second. Also suppose that one of these nodes sends a message of length $L = 10^6$ bits to another node on the link. Then, the time delay for the first node to transmit all 1,000 bits out of that device is $t_{trans} = L/R = \{10^6 \text{ bits}\}/10_{10}$ bits per second $= 10^{-4}$ sec $= 0.1$ milliseconds.

Again, a delay of 0.1 msec is the time required for all the message bits to exit the first node, not the time required for the second node to receive the full message. To compute the full delay in sending this message between these two nodes on the network, consider a specific case regarding the distance of separation between the two nodes. Suppose that these two nodes are separated by a distance of $D = 40$ km. Thus, the corresponding propagation delay described in the previous subsection is $t_{prop} = D/s = 0.2$ milliseconds. This result gives a total delay of $t_{total} = t_{trans} + t_{prop} = 0.3$ milliseconds, which corresponds to the total interval between the transmission of the first bit of the message out of the first node and the reception of the final bit of this message at the second node.

Another relevant factor in the computation of the transmission is the scheme for sending multiple segments of a message. Suppose that a given application layer message is being sent on an Ethernet data link between the two nodes, which permits a MTU of 1,500 bytes = 12,000 bits. Assume that the fragmentation of the original application layer message yields six different transport layer segments. Also, assume that six different corresponding data link layer frames are generated for the data link connecting the two subject nodes under consideration, after the headers and trailers are added from the various layers of the protocol stack. It is necessary to send six frames, wherein each of the first five are of length 12,000 bits, and the sixth frame accommodates the remaining bits of the original message, to send the full message over the subject data link. To simplify the discussion, assume that this sixth frame is also of length 12,000 bits.

There exist two primary waiting schemes for sending these six transport layer segments over a network. One is stop-and-wait, and the second is pipelining. First, we examine *stop-and-wait*, where the sender waits to receive the acknowledgment corresponding to a given transport layer segment before sending the subsequent fragment of the full original message.

For this scenario, the summation of the transmission and propagation delay gives a total delay interval of 0.3 milliseconds between the transmission of the first bit of the first segment from the first node, and the reception of the last bit of the first segment at the second node. However, under the stop-and-wait scheme, the first node will not transmit the second segment of the full message until it receives an acknowledgement (ACK) of the receipt of the first segment. A relatively lightweight message comprised of just header and trailer information can be used to send this acknowledgement from the second node back to the first, so it is often reasonable to neglect the transmission delay of sending this acknowledgement packet back to the first node. However, in many cases, the time interval for the propagation of the acknowledgment packet is not negligible, which incurs an additional 0.2 milliseconds of delay. That is, under the stop-and-wait scheme, a total of 0.5 milliseconds of delay is incurred in sending and acknowledging the first segment, before the second segment can begin transmitting out of the first node. Then, the sending node can begin transmitting the second segment to the receiving node, which also incurs an additional delay of 0.3 milliseconds between the instant that the sending node transmits the first bit of the second segment, and the receipt of the last bit at the receiving node. Again, a lightweight acknowledgment packet gives an additional 0.2 milliseconds of delay in sending and acknowledging this second segment of the six segments. The delays incurred by the other fragments of the original message are additive in this manner for the stop-and-wait scheme, so that a total delay of 3 milliseconds is incurred in sending all six segments of the original message across the two subject nodes of the network. In addition, it should be clear that the effective data rate R_{eff} is significantly smaller than the maximum possible data rate R just due to the suboptimal acknowledgment scheme that is used in sending the data.

A more optimal scheme for sending multiple fragments of a larger message is that of *pipelining*. For the pipeline strategy, the receiving station effectively allocates credit to the sending station, so that this node can transmit a second segment, and perhaps a third, and fourth, before receiving the acknowledgement packet corresponding to the first fragment. In this manner, there is only a single effective roundtrip time delay that covers all the segments that can be sent under the advertised credit. Assume that the receiving node allocates 36,000 bits of credit to the sending station. Then, this node can transmit the first three segments, each of length 12,000 bits in sequence with one segment immediately following the previous one. A pipeline strategy aids in maintaining the effective data rate to be at, or near, the optimal data rate that is possible for a given link between the two nodes.

8.3.3 Router Processing Delay

A third type of primary delay in packet networks is the processing delay incurred at routers. A primary function of a router is to receive incoming data packets and then send them out of appropriate interfaces with the router according to the network addressing. Assume that a given message arrives at an interface from a LAN. The processing at the router will perform calculations based upon the layer 3 IP address to determine the appropriate interface for transmitting the data packet to be sent towards its next destination.

Figure 8.5 shows a simplified network involving the connection of a border router R0 to a LAN containing four users {A, B, C, D}. The router R0 is, in turn, connected to three other routers {R1, R2, R3} through interfaces {1, 2, 3}, respectively. Next,

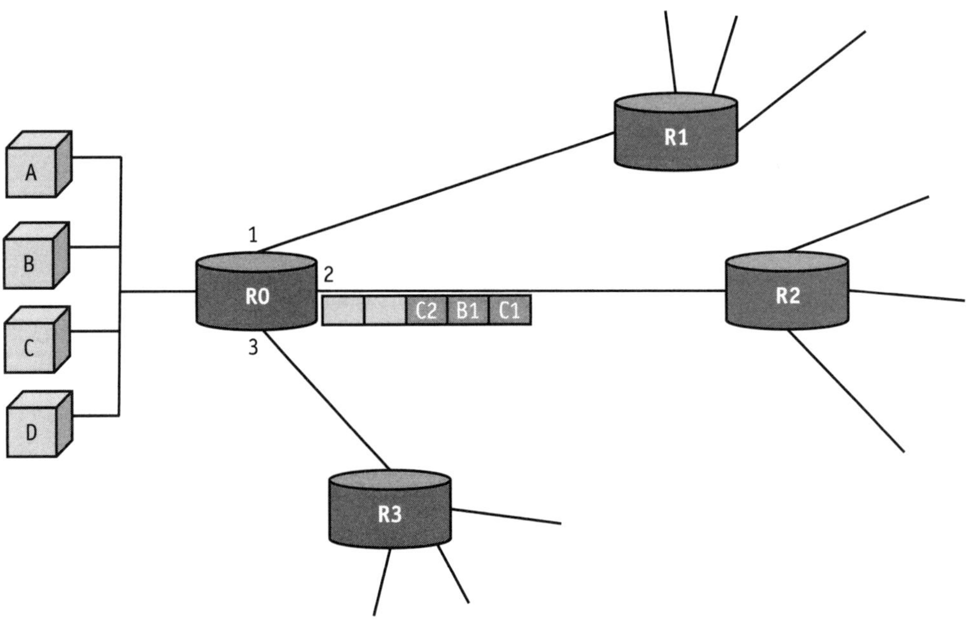

Figure 8.5
Simplified network with four users {A, B, C, D} connected to border router R0.

assume that a particular message arrives at router R0 from one of the users. This router must perform processing based upon the destination address within the packet to determine the appropriate outgoing interface for this packet. Effectively, the router searches through its router table to find the entry with the best match to the destination address. In Figure 8.5, the incoming packet is retransmitted out of one of the three possible interfaces {1, 2, 3}. As such, the calculations of the communication processing at a given router constitutes a third type delay for messages in a packet network. In addition, for normal packet network operations, a given packet is retransmitted out of each router it encounters in traversing the network. An additional contribution to the transmission delay is incurred for each router encountered along its path of traversal from the original sending station to its final receiving station.

8.3.4 Queuing Delay

Figure 8.5 also shows an example of a fourth type of delay that occurs in datagram networks, which is queuing delay. In particular, the various users on a local area network are often supported by relatively fast transmission speeds, as with high-speed Ethernet involving speeds of up to $R \cong 100$ GHz or more. Thus, messages sent from any one of the four users {A, B, C, D} can arrive very quickly at the border router R0 for this LAN. However, the connection from R0 to the open internet is much slower. As such, congestion often occurs at the border router so a queuing strategy is used to hold input messages in local memory until transmission resources are available out of the appropriate interface for router R0.

In Figure 8.5, three data packets {B1, C1, B2} have already arrived and are awaiting transmission out of the second interface. These packets arrived in the second interface queue in the order {B1, C1, B2} and thus will be transmitted out of this interface in the same order. These messages are permitted to have drastically different lengths, as some messages can be header messages with little or no payload, and others can have significant data payloads. Since the transmission delay is proportional to the packet length L, longer packets ahead in the queue contribute to longer queuing delay. Also, a greater number of the prior unsent packets in the queue imply that any new packets just arriving at the router in question will incur a longer queuing delay. A further difficulty arrives if the queue becomes completely full, followed by the arrival of newly incoming packets to the router. Then, the router typically discards such packets, and it is often necessary for the upper layer protocols to recognize that a given packet was dropped or lost and thus must be resent.

To model the queuing system, there is a wait line queue and a service line server that processes the items as packets r as shown in Figure 8.6. Queuing theory is based on Little's law for the queuing system length Q ($Q = \lambda T$), where the item arrival rate λ determines the resident time the item waits in the queue ($Q_w = \lambda T_w$), while the departure rate μ determines the service time as a function of utilization ρ ($\rho = 1/\mu$). The system delay of the queue is the sum of the wait time and the service time:

$$T = T_w + T_s = T_w + \rho \tag{8.1}$$

The common modeling of queuing systems has three elements: the number of servers N, whether there is discarding of items δ, and the distribution analysis. Given the known algebraic equations, there are many tables, routines, and calculators available.

For the number of services N, the arrival rate to the queue stays the same, but the utilization is a function of the number of servers:

$$T = T_w + T_s = T_w + N\rho \tag{8.2}$$

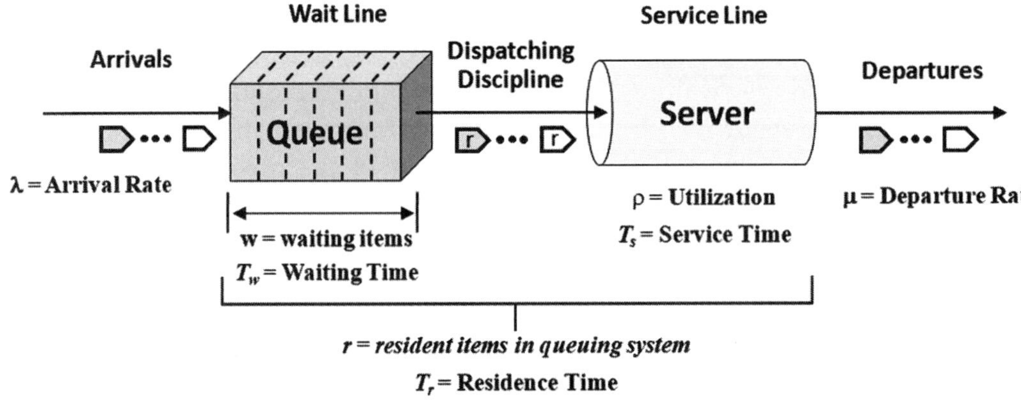

Figure 8.6
Simplified queuing network.

A modification of Little's Law is the Erlang function with a Poisson arrival rate distribution, first-in first-out (FIFO) dispatching, and exponential analysis. To account for the dropout of the system using the Erlang function, then the queue length is:

$$Q = \frac{\lambda - \delta}{\mu} = (\lambda - \delta)\rho \tag{8.3}$$

With the exponential processing rate distributions, the queue wait time T_w is the proportion of arrivals that are served without dropout:

$$\frac{\lambda}{\mu} = e^{-T_w \mu} \tag{8.4}$$

and thus:

$$T_w = \frac{1}{\mu}\mathrm{Ln}\left(\frac{\lambda}{\mu}\right) = \rho\mathrm{Ln}(\lambda\rho) \tag{8.5}$$

There are three types of distribution analysis using Kendall's notation for queuing analysis of X/Y/N where X is the distribution of interarrival times, Y is the distribution of service times, and N is the number of services. The notational commonly used are:

G = general distribution of interarrival times or service times;

G1 = general independent distribution of interarrival times;

M = exponential distribution;

D = deterministic arrivals or fixed-length service.

For example, standard notations in the queuing formulas are M/M/1, M/M/N, M/G/1, M/G1/1, and M/D/1. In a general sense, a single wait line queue that includes many single M/M/1 servers that can be considered as time division multiplexing (TDM), while multiple wait lines each with a dedicated M/M/1 server can be considered as space division multiplexing (SDM). Figure 8.7 shows a M/M/2 versus the two M/M/1 queues. The queuing tables have defined equations for the analysis based on these principles for the average value, Q, probability of items ($Pr\,[q < m]$), as well as variance σ_Q. Formulas can be found in queuing tables.

Using the chapter example of six frames with 12,000 bits each, with an arrival rate λ of 100,000 bits per second (bps), and departure rate μ = 10,000 bps:

$$T = Q/\lambda + 1/\mu$$

T = (72000 bits)/(100000 bps) + 1/(100 bps) = 0.72 + 0.01 = 0.73 seconds

An interesting analysis is that of whether all the data must go through one server (M/M/1) versus having multiple servers (M/M/N), such as bank line (one queue and multiple servers) and a grocery store line (multiple queues with multiple servers). Analysis of these scenarios reveals that having one queue with multiple servers optimizes the results as the orchestration of processing is dispatched to the available server, while the long packets assigned to different queues could delay processing as the server for that queue is longer and other queue/servers are idle.

8.4 Summary

This chapter discussed essential features and mechanisms of transmission and receptions of signals within packet networks. First, such RF energy for such signals can be well localized along lines of communication, as in wired networks. In contrast, wireless networks involve the transmission and reception of RF signal energy into less localized open environments.

In addition, this chapter provides a discussion of the form and function of the five layers of the standard TCP/IP enterprise networks used in the open internet. Here, the data link layer 2 effectively ensures that groups of bits can traverse the medium of the physical layer 1 joining two adjacent nodes. The network layer 3 contains the addressing needed to send data packets across a complicated world-wide network. The transport layer 4 contains the port addressing needed to support multiple programs at the application layer 5.

Finally, this chapter discussed the four primary contributions to the delay between the initial transmission at the sending station and the final reception at the receiving station. The propagation delay is based upon the total traversed distance, and the transmission delay is the time required for a given node to modulate all the data within the packet out of the device. The router processing delay occurs due to the computations necessary to determine the appropriate output interface required to forward a given packet. Finally, queuing delay can yield additional delay, especially for border routers that are attempting to send data from within the LAN to the broader internet.

References

[1] Wu, Chwan-Hwa J., and Irwin, J. D., *Introduction to Computer Networks and Cybersecurity*, Boca Raton, FL: CRC Press, 2013.

[2] Stallings, W., *Data and Computer Communications*, Tenth Edition, Upper Saddle River, NJ: Pearson, 2014.

[3] Chandra, P., *Bulletproof Wireless Security: GSM, UMTS, 802.11, and Ad Hoc Security*, Burlington, MA: Elsevier, 2005.

9

Machine Learning for RF Signal Classification

9.1 Introduction

In this chapter, we present signal classification revolutionized by modern ML techniques. Signal classification involves understanding features of various signals and how these features can be utilized to differentiate one signal from another. A signal can be differentiated based on modulation schemes such as pulse, amplitude, phase, and/or frequency. Within these schemes, further distinction can separate one signal from another. For example, within a frequency modulation scheme, a signal could be linear frequency modulated (LFM) or nonlinear frequency modulated (NLFM); within a phase modulated signal, a signal could be composed of biphase or polyphase. Hence, the goal of machine learning algorithms is detecting and classifying various signals of interest based on their composition. It is important to understand that diversity of signals or waveforms has evolved based on their utilization of different tasks. For example, Wi-Fi signals, Bluetooth signals, radio frequency data communication signals, radar waveforms, aircraft, and GPS waveforms all have different characteristics. These signals, in turn, aid in identifying the existence of a device in certain environments. Researchers have investigated various ML techniques to classify signals; however, recently deep neural networks have been of great interest as DNN models are more robust and perform well in classifying signals. This chapter develops the following concepts:

RF signals, ML algorithms, deep neural networks, signal classification, RF signal datasets, and a deep learning implementation of RF signal classification.

9.2 RF Signal Classification Problems

The DARPA Radio Frequency Machine Learning Systems (RFMLS) program is the first major program to embrace modern machine learning techniques for signal classification. DARPA observed the huge advancement of ML algorithms in the domains of vision, hearing, and languages. They also found that progress in these areas has been significant in recent years, surpassing human abilities in some ways. Though the RF environment presents familiar ground for ML researchers, there are important differences that make RF ML problems unique:

- Compared to other domains, the RF data rate is much higher. A high-definition video stream at 60 Hz could be on the order of 3 Gbps (ignoring coding compression savings). One GHz of RF spectrum data has approximately ten times that data rate, and is not nearly as amenable to decimation to improve processing.
- RF waveforms are typically captured and represented as complex numbers, underscoring the importance of both amplitude and phase of the signal. Although there has been interest recently in complex-valued neural networks, the technology for learning naturally in the complex plane is not fully developed and relies on treating complex variables as two real numbers.
- The RF environment offers a more compelling reason for developing a native complex-valued approach.

DARPA put the RF signal classification problems into four major tasks: (1) Feature Learning—the ability to learn features necessary to perform a discrimination task directly from sensor data, (2) Attention and Saliency—the ability to have top-down (task-driven) attention guide which RF samples are ultimately most important to the system's task, complemented by a bottom-up (data-driven) mechanism able to direct attention to new signals of interest, (3) Autonomous RF Sensor Configuration—the ability to autonomously reconfigure an RF sensor (e.g., center frequency tuning, beamforming direction, analog sensor reconfiguration) to create the RF data required to improve overall task performance, and (4) Waveform Synthesis—the ability of an RF system to learn to transmit entirely new waveforms to achieve a task.

9.2.1 RF Feature Learning

The modern Internet of Things relies on each networked device to honestly present a digital ID (identification). However, digital IDs (in software and firmware) can be cloned, so IoT security would benefit if it were supplemented by a unique physical ID intrinsic to the device. RF transmitters are naturally imperfect devices due to the tolerances in manufacturing the analog electronics. A *radiofrequency fingerprint* (RFFP) for each transmitting device can be measured. The communications security literature has many examples of the RFFP concept. The typical research centers around a few nominally identical transmitters of a single protocol type and studies their transmit signals to hand-engineer features that discriminate the individual transmitters. While successful as proof-of-concept demonstrations, hand-engineered-feature discriminators have not been shown to support the number of devices expected in IoT populations. Similarly, hand-engineering approaches that focus on only a single type of RF system (e.g., Wi-Fi) will not handle the diversity of wireless protocols emerging in the IoT.

Hence the research problem is developing a trainable system that can distinguish between thousands (1,000 to 10,000) of RF devices that are nominally identical. Since these signals are indistinguishable using conventional hand-engineered RF signal features (e.g., modulation type, rate), the ML algorithm must learn more abstract features, which are imparted to the intended RF signal by the RF transmit chain and associated hardware. The trainable system must be general such that it is applicable to multiple wireless communications protocols. The algorithms should be robust in training conditions, which include varied signal-to-noise level, adjacent channel interference, cochannel interference, and wireless channel effects on the signals of interest.

9.2.2 Attention and Saliency

Next-generation RF systems must evolve from characterizing megahertz of spectrum to characterizing gigahertz of spectrum. To do this, RFML systems must have a sense of which signals are important, focusing processing resources on those signals, and conserving resources by disregarding other ones that are unimportant for a particular task. We must develop algorithms that can learn important versus unimportant signals and their associated labels. Different systems should operate entirely differently on the same dataset, depending on how the system is trained.

For example, consider a dataset that contains both communications systems and radar systems. Under one training modality, the system might learn communications signals that are important and report the modulation associated with them. Under a different modality, the system might learn radar signals that are important and identify them simply with the name of the radar system.

9.2.3 Autonomous RF Sensor Configurations

Much of the early research in adaptive RF systems focused on analog electronics (i.e., the RF front end), building systems that can be reconfigured, so that the operating characteristics are not set in stone at design time. Similarly, recent advances have resulted in large-scale, all-digital RF systems that are intrinsically flexible. These advances are largely untapped because there has been little focus on coupling this adaptability with the necessary intelligence to reconfigure the RF sensor for better performance of the overall system task. Learning for autonomous control has revolutionized game playing and self-driving cars. Although the sensors and actuators are different in RF applications, an RFML system can learn to optimize the huge number of possible configurations (analog electronics, beam-steering angle, bandwidth sensitivity, position, etc.).

9.2.4 Waveform Synthesis

Tasks such as waveform generation in present-day RF systems amounts to decisions on a small set of discrete choices—use waveform A, or use waveform B. However, this strategy fails to achieve true waveform synthesis, which is the ability to generate wholly new waveforms. Discrete selection approaches are akin to a speech-generation system preprogrammed with a discrete set of words from which it can choose. Such a system cannot pronounce new words or apply more nuanced concepts such as syllabic stress, common in modern speech-synthesis systems. Similar challenges exist in the RF domain in coping with very large decision spaces. ML approaches, which enable unsupervised or semi-/self-supervised learning of efficient waveform encodings, enable RFML systems to learn new waveforms able to achieve one or more simultaneous objectives.

9.3 An Overview of Machine Learning Algorithms

ML has been used for dimensionality reduction, structure prediction, and anomaly detection. Over the years, ML algorithms have evolved from handcrafted knowledge to describe the data, to statistical processing to categorize the data, towards methods of contextual analysis for explicability. ML-based expert systems of the 1970s and 1980s helped physicians diagnose diseases based on probabilistic outcome provided by the neural network classifier. In the 1990s, statistical reasoning was combined with NN models to analyze radio frequency sensor data such as synthetic aperture radar (SAR) imagery to detect and classify targets. In general, ML techniques support: (1) analysts who are making decisions in a complex space (e.g., internet analysis of various users from social media), (2) operators who routinely have to exploit large imagery data (e.g., identifying target behaviors), and (3) users who make decisions for technical help (e.g., driving a car). Recently, deep learning has shown better accuracy in image and text recognition in research challenge problems versus that of traditional methods. Hence, each of the ML/DL methods provide some benefits that are important, including:

- *Accuracy:* Improving performance over analysts conducting similar tasks.
- *Execution:* Solving big data problems in real-time versus manual operation.
- *Complex problem solution:* Resolving complex problems over many options that are nearly impossible for everyday users.
- *Image classification:* Automatic target recognition, classification, and identification.

- *Natural language processing:* Target semantic labeling with a dictionary.
- *Autonomous systems:* Pointing the sensor for command and control.
- *Sentiment analysis:* Optimizing the collection parameters for a given scenario.
- *Biomedical applications:* Decision support for a subject-matter expert.

Machine learning algorithms involve offline (training) and online (testing), as shown in Figure 9.1. For the offline system, a large set of training data (e.g., 80%) is used to train the methods/models, while testing data comprises the remaining fraction of the data (20%). The samples for training are typically labeled to resolve the salient features and the resulting statistical classifier. The features represent something in the data that for 1-D signals are peaks, and for 2-D images are shapes and lines. As the data becomes more complex, such as in natural language processing, then various sets of features are formed as a file of words and stored in a dictionary.

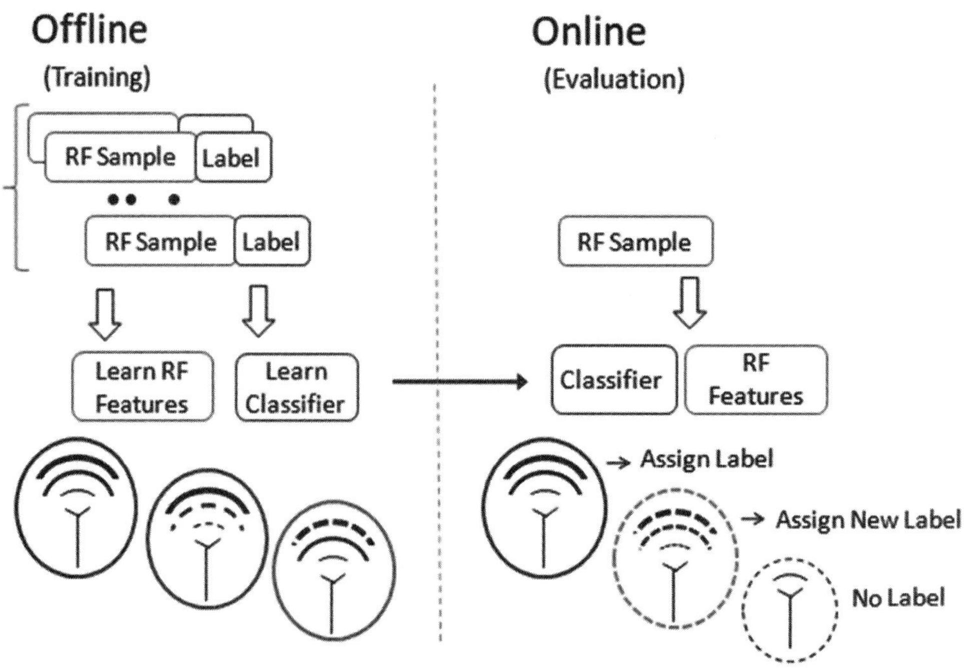

Figure 9.1
Offline training and online evaluation.

As a *dictionary* provides a lookup for semantic content, a dictionary of features provides physical attributes of the sensor information based on context. Training thus seeks to build a dictionary offline for the features used in online analysis.

Using the classifier and a set of features, the online evaluation brings in a new measurement sample and determines: (1) if it is in the dictionary, assign a label (e.g., target), (2) if not in the dictionary but representative of the content in the dictionary, assign a new label (e.g., confuser), or (3) represents a measurement or observation that should not be in the dictionary (e.g., no label). Inherent in the analysis is the label output quality, from which traditionally has been probability of correct classification (PCC), or probability of identification (PID), for a label.

The development of many machine learning algorithms derives from the methods used to train the algorithm, explain the results, and/or determine performance. Inherent in the discussion are the data used for training, of which some is labeled (e.g., offline data collection) and some is unlabeled (e.g., online streaming analysis). Another factor to consider is repeatability, in which the statistical analysis clearly provides a verification of the weightings and interpretability for explanations. The third factor is performance, which should be conducted not only in standardized conditions (SOCs) such as radio frequency, modulation type, and collection geometry, but also in extended operating conditions (EOCs) such as environment conditions due to various sources of noise and clutter. The performance analysis is typically provided by metrics such as accuracy. Table 9.1 presents more details on the categories of many ML methods. ML applications leverage traditional approaches for clustering, classification, and regression, while other attributes include dimension reduction and data association. With the advent of contemporary neural network methods, Figure 9.2 organizes these ML techniques from linear classifiers to nonlinear classifiers that include many of the popular NN approaches.

9.4 Deep Neural Networks

A deep neural network is a NN with many deep hidden layers that are used for nonlinear data classification, as shown in Figure 1.2 in Chapter 1. In each successive layer, the NN learns more descriptive

Table 9.1
Details of ML Methods, Based on Domains, Training, and Testing Types

Type	Subtype	Methods
Supervised	Regression	Linear regression Nonlinear regression Gaussian process regression (GPR) Ensemble methods Decision trees Neural networks
	Classification	Support vector machine (SVM) Linear discriminant analysis (LDA) k-nearest neighbor (kNN) Artificial neural networks (ANN) Naïve Bayes Random forest
Semisupervised		Semisupervised SVM Graph-based label propagation Generative methods Active learning Transfer learning
Unsupervised	Clustering	K-means, K-manifolds Random forest Fuzzy C-means Agglomeration hierarchical Kernel density-based Gaussian mixture models (GMM) Hidden Markov models (HMM) Self-organized maps (SOM) Neural networks
	Dimension reduction	Principal component analysis (PCA) Kernel proposal component analysis Multidimensional scaling Maximum variance unfolding Isomap Local linear embedding (LLE) Diffusion maps Local tangent space alignment (LSTA)
	Association	A prior Bayesian data fusion Evidential reasoning Multihypothesis association
Reinforcement learning		Epsilon greedy Prioritize sweeping Temporal difference Q-learning

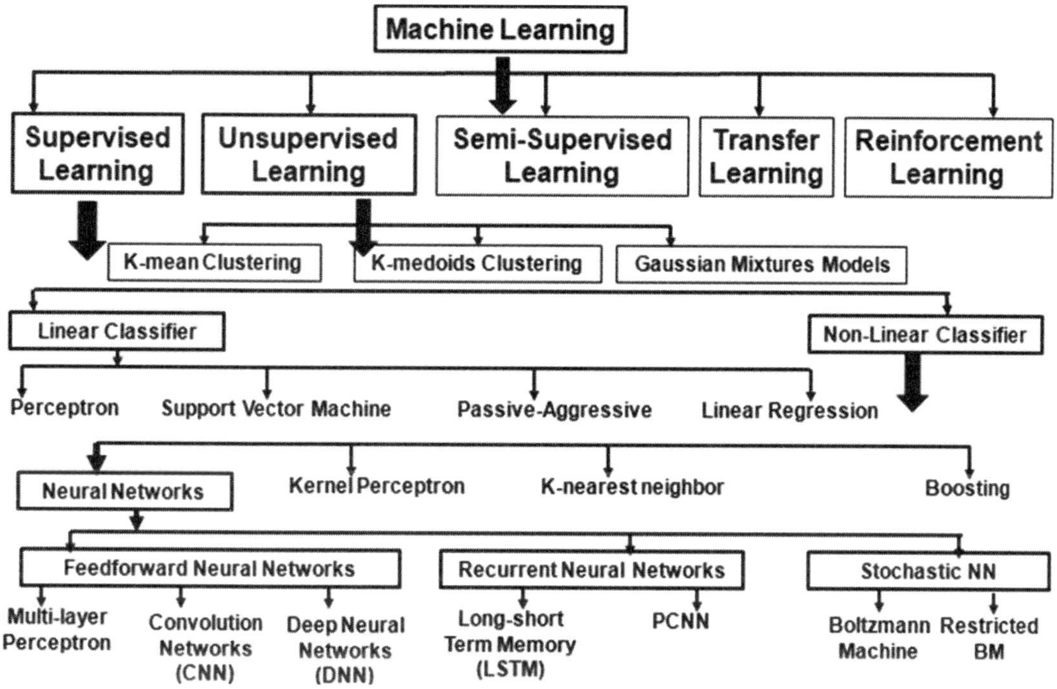

Figure 9.2
ML methods by category.

features. Eventually, the successive feature learning from each layer supports a more discriminative classification.

With diagrams showing many arrows passing data from one node to another node in another layer, as in Figure 1.2, DNN is typically shown as in Figure 9.3. The DNN is fully connected, with input, hidden, and output layers. The input layer learns to perform preprocessing on the input from a set of features. The data is then sent to a series of hidden layers, where the number of layers can vary and is determined by design. As the data propagates through hidden layers, more complex features are extracted and learned. The output layer performs classification and determines the label of the input. For classification, the last layer usually employs a *soft-max* function that normalizes the probability distribution to a fixed number of probabilities.

DNNs are one form of deep learning methods applied to classify image, signal, or speech data. Other DNN methods are shown in Figure 9.4 [6]. One of the most prominent ones is autoencoder

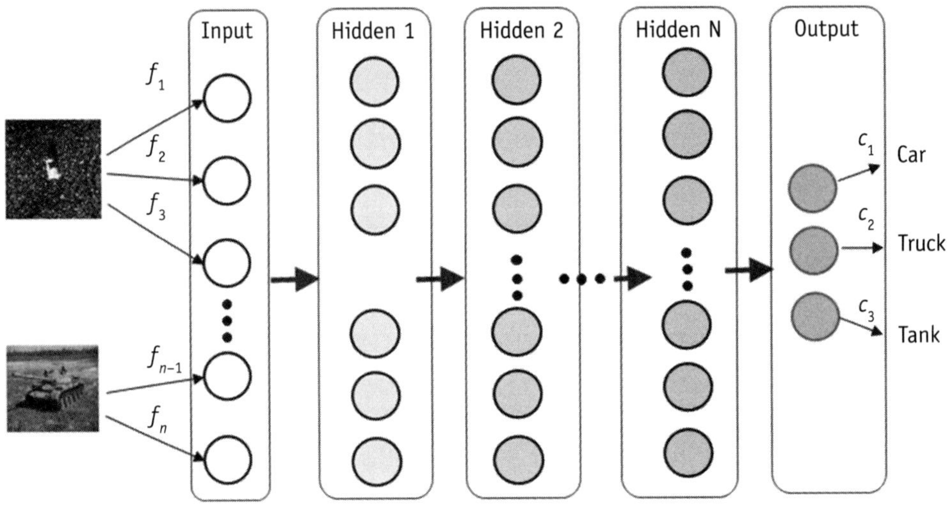

Figure 9.3
DNN model representation.

(AE) which both encodes and decodes data features as parameters for learning. Within the *generative methods* category are deterministic deep belief networks (DBN) and stochastic deep Boltzmann machines (DBM). To afford robust analysis and adaptation to real-world conditions, stochastic analysis enhances DL methods.

Some of the important DNN models/architectures are shown in Table 9.2. These models can be modified (adding more layers/parameters) for performance tuning. Many of these DNNs use convolution filters for feature extraction as well as for discrimination.

For image classification problems, DNN architectures use convolution. Hence, the DNN architectures in Table 9.2 are built on

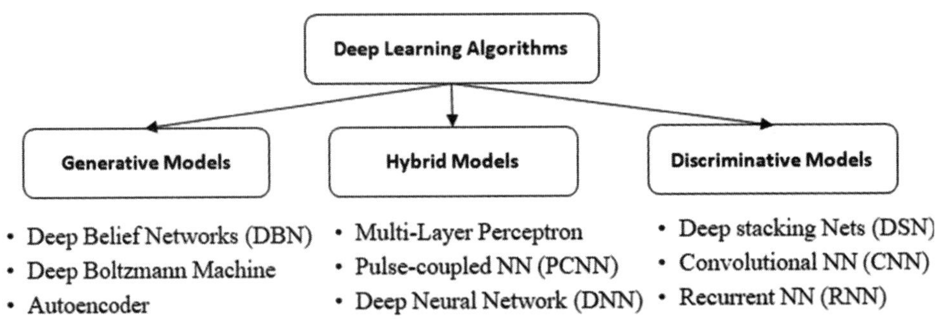

Figure 9.4
Deep learning methods.

Table 9.2
Classical Deep Neural Networks

Method	Convolutional Layers	Reference	
AlexNet	5	Krizhevsky et al., 2012	[1]
VGG (visual geometry group)	19	Simonyan et al., 2014	[2]
GoogleNet	22	Szegedy et al., 2015	[3]
ResNet (residual network)	34	He et al., 2015	[4]

convolutional neural networks (CNN). CNN includes choosing a kernel as a receptive field filter (e.g., a 5 × 5 bounding box in an image), learning the classification, and typically employing back-propagation with stochastic gradient descent to learn one layer at a time. During the forward pass, each filter is convolved across the width and height of the input volume by computing the dot product between the input and the filter elements to produce a 2-D activation map. Essentially, *network convolution* learns the best filters that activate when it detects a specific feature type for a given spatial input position. By connecting all the convolution layer results, reasonable classifications are obtained subject to the appropriate choice of the number of layers. More exemplar data increases the likelihood the system would be able to perform well with increasingly complex situations. The optimum number of layers in CNN is part of ongoing work.

In CNN, the convolution and fully connected layers perform linear transformations on their inputs [6]. Figure 9.5 highlights the

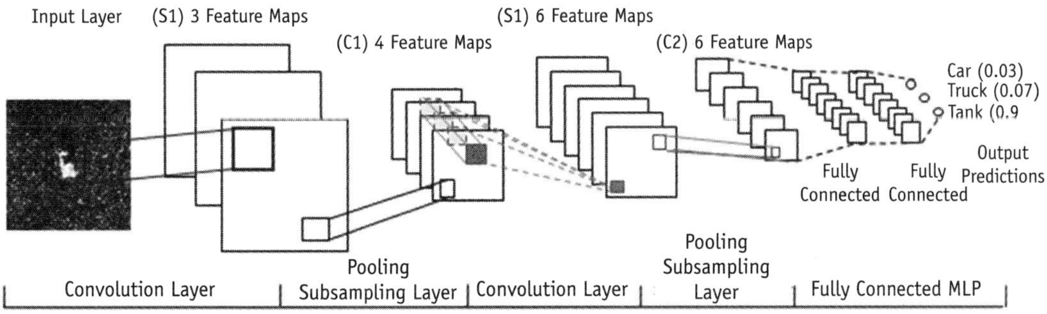

Figure 9.5
CNN concept.

typical layers of a CNN architecture that begins with the convolution layer, followed by additional layers of sampling and convolutions. Using the activation and pooling layers introduces nonlinearity that search the input space for very specific features. Each filter creates a feature map that gets fed into the next layer to be filtered again. CNNs create very high-dimensional representations of inputs depending upon the number of filters that are used, and as a result, must be resized with pooling and down-sampling layers. Finally, a fully connected final layer determines the output training classifications. CNN is widely accepted as a contemporary DL method, showing great promise for radio frequency classification.

Convolution Layers

A convolution layer convolves the result: $C = I*F$ where it is pointwise multiplication (row*column) of the image I pixel values and the filter F. For example, from Figure 9.6, we can derive convolutional results of a segment of an image with a filter as:

$$\begin{aligned}\begin{bmatrix} 0 & 0 & 0 \\ 0 & 0 & 0 \\ 0 & 0 & \mathbf{1} \end{bmatrix} * \begin{bmatrix} 1 & -1 & -1 \\ -1 & 1 & -1 \\ -1 & -1 & \mathbf{1} \end{bmatrix} &= \left[0(1)+0(-1)+0(-1)\right] \\ &+\left[0(-1)+0(1)+0(-1)\right]+\left[0(-1)+0(-1)+(\mathbf{1})(\mathbf{1})\right]=1\end{aligned} \tag{9.1}$$

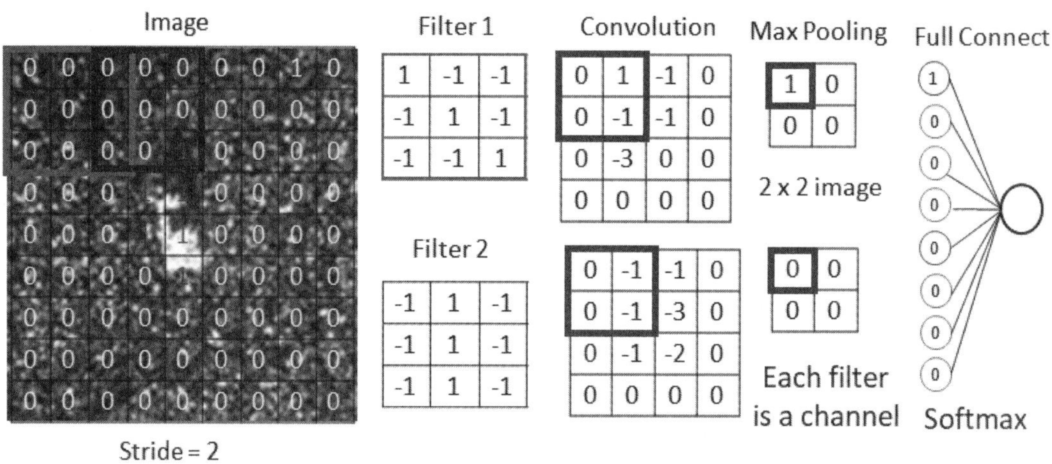

Figure 9.6
CNN example.

Pooling Layers

The pooling layer spatially resizes the input and operates independently on every input depth. The most common filter size is 2 × 2 where a stride of $S = 2$ downsamples at every input depth slice in the input by 2 along both width and height, discarding 75% of the activations. Using the *rectified linear unit* (ReLU), the nonsaturating activation function $f(x) = \max(0, x)$ removes negative values from an activation map by setting them to zero. The max function increases the nonlinear properties of the overall network decision without affecting the receptive fields of the convolution layer. In Figure 9.6, each filter of the pooling layer goes from 8 × 8 to 2 × 2.

Fully Connected Layers

Neurons in a fully connected layer have connections to all activations in the previous layer. The activations are given by a matrix multiplication followed by a vector addition of a bias offset. The final layer is the *loss layer*, which penalizes the deviation between the predicted (output) and the true labels.

DropOut Layer

To prevent overfitting, at each training stage, individual nodes are either dropped out of the net with probability $(1 - p)$ or kept with probability p, reducing the network size. In the training stages, the probability that a hidden node will be dropped is usually 0.5, from which the network is trained. The removed nodes are then reinserted into the network with their original weights for testing. The use of a dropout layer improves training speed by reducing node interactions, allowing them to learn more robust features that better generalize to new data.

9.5 RF Signal Dataset for Wi-Fi Fingerprinting

Northeastern University published (https://genesys-lab.org/oracle) a dataset, deep learning model, and associated paper for conducting research and development for Wi-Fi signal-based emitter detection and classification (i.e., RF fingerprinting of devices). This dataset, called ORACLE, is generated for RF fingerprinting of radios from a large pool of bit-similar devices (same hardware, protocol, physical address, MAC ID) using only I/Q samples at the physical layer.

The dataset (see [5]) consists of recordings of raw I/Q samples from 16, high-end X310 USRP SDRs with the same B210 radio as a receiver. The recordings are categorized into different folders with folder name "*xxft*," where *xx* represents the transmitter-receiver separation distance in feet. Each recording has a dataset file with an extension of *.sigmf-data*, and a metadata file with an extension of *.sigmf-meta*. These files are named in a specific format for more intuitive understanding. For example, the dataset file *WiFi_air_X310_3123D7B_2ft_run1* represents:

- *Wi-Fi:* IEEE802.11a standard-compliant WLAN frame;
- *air:* Medium of transmission;
- *X310:* The type of USRP radio;
- *3123D7B:* Device serial ID;
- *2ft:* The transmitter-receiver separation distance in feet;
- *run1:* The recording number;
- *sigmf-data/sigmf-meta:* The extension of dataset file/metadata file.

The ORACLE dataset can train convolutional neural networks using I/Q samples collected from an experimental setup of USRP SDRs, as shown in Figure 9.7, with a fixed USRP B210 as the receiver. As previously mentioned, all transmitters are bit-similar USRP X310 radios that emit IEEE 802.11a standards-compliant frames generated via a MATLAB WLAN system toolbox. The data frames generated contain random payloads but have the same address fields

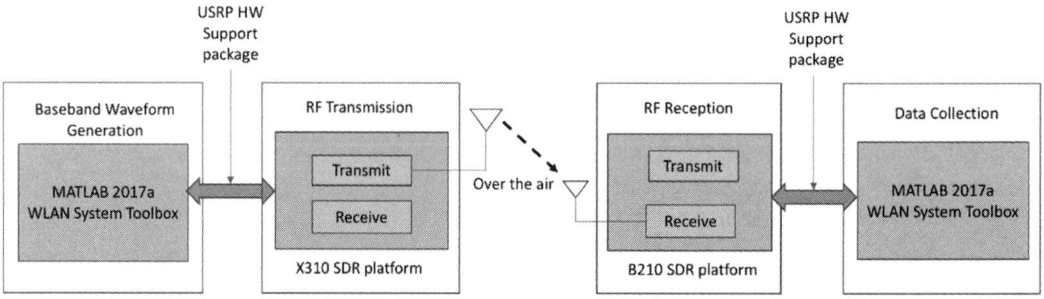

Figure 9.7
Northeastern University's experimental setup for Wi-Fi data collection.

and are then streamed to the selected SDR for over-the-air wireless transmission. The receiver SDR samples the incoming signals at 5 MS/s sampling rate at the center frequency of 2.45 GHz for Wi-Fi. They collect over 20 million samples for each radio; and run the experiments in a more open area that has fewer reflections as shown in Figure 9.8. The transmitter-receiver separation distance is increased from 2 ft to 62 ft with an interval of 6 ft. These datasets can be used by researchers to reproduce the original work (as presented in their paper), or to further explore other machine learning problems in the domain of wireless communication.

9.6 Deep-Learning-Based Wi-Fi Signal Classification

In this section, we present a deep learning implementation of Wi-Fi signal detection and classification using the ORACLE dataset published by Northeastern University. A baseline DL implementation of RF fingerprinting using NU data can be found in the github

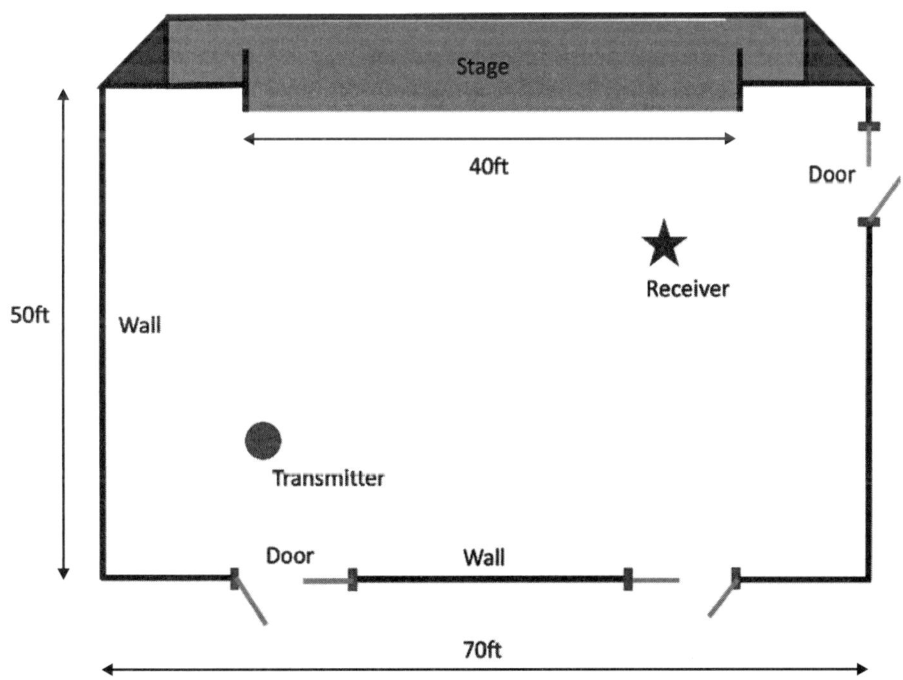

Figure 9.8
NU experimental environment: open area with much less reflection.

repository (https://github.com/neu-spiral/RFMLS-NEU). We used Google's TensorFlow DL software framework for CNN implementation of RF fingerprinting (i.e., emitter detection and classification), as shown in Figure 9.9.

RF Signal Data Preparation

- Preprocess the raw signal data (see Figure 9.10): Before preprocessing, the signal is not shifted to baseband, so the dark vertical line is around direct current (DC). After preprocessing, the signal has been shifted to baseband so signal center frequency (2.45 GHz) is centered rather than DC.
- Selected one of the preprocessed TFRecord shards to use for a focused training attempt:
  - Selected record shard 10 from the closest (2 ft) Tx/Rx distance recording set.
  - Shards contain approximately 4,800 examples (128 samples, nonoverlapping, I/Q clips) from each of the 16 different transmitters for classification.
- Split-record shard into a training and test set:
  - Training: First 4,000 examples from each Tx (total of 64k).
  - Test: Final (approximately) 800 examples (total of approximately 12k).
  - During training, a random 10% of training sets were used for validation.
- Prior to training, the mean and standard deviation of the training data is calculated and used to center/whiten both the training and test sets.

Deep-Learning Model Preparation

- The model provided in the NU code we used was Baseline2D, consisting of:

Figure 9.9
The overall algorithmic implementation steps for Google's TensorFlow DL software framework.

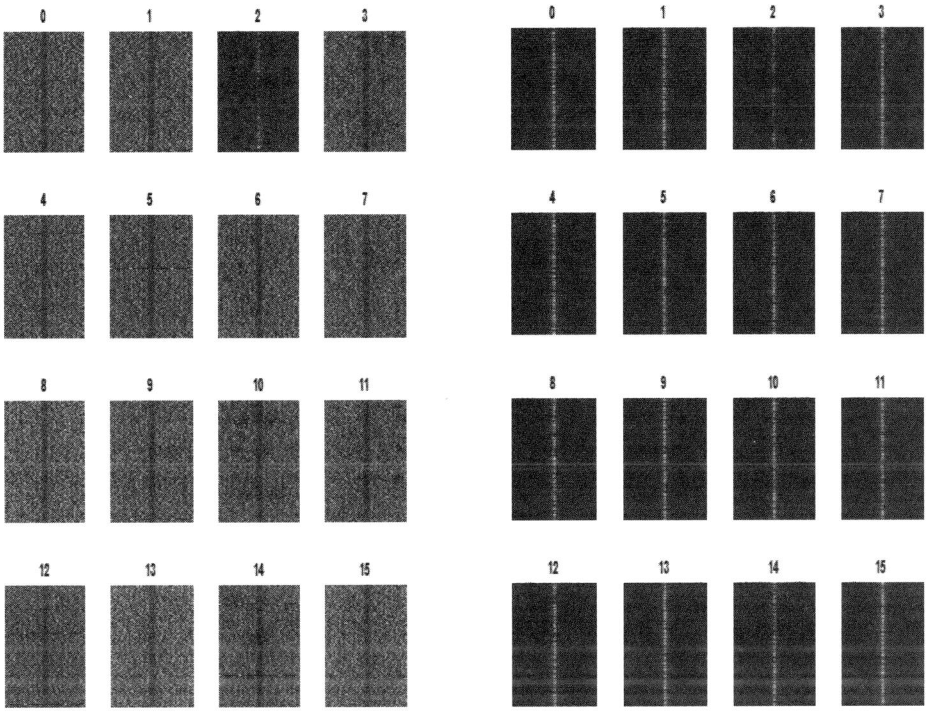

Figure 9.10
Spectrum of the signal before (left), and after (right).

- Six convolutional layers in pairs of two, pairs followed by a max-pool layer.
- A flatten operation followed by three fully connected layers.
- Each internal neuron layer followed by a ReLU, with a softmax applied to the 16-output neurons for classification.
- Dropout is used on the fully connected layers.

Updated Deep-Learning Model and Training

- We modified the NU model with different kernel/layer arrangement consisting of:
  - Six convolution layers, followed by ReLU;
  - Three fully connected layers, using ReLU for hidden layers and softmax for the 16-output neurons;
  - Using batch normalization instead of dropout;

- The model is trained with initial learning rate of 0.0001, batch size of 128, using the Adam optimizer and categorical cross-entropy loss;
- Early stopping based on validation-loss monitoring is used, and the learning rate is reduced on validation-loss plateau of three steps or more;
- Following (Table 9.3) are the details of DNN model configurations.

Results

Figures 9.11 and 9.12 reveal that this model/training setup achieved approximately 90% training and 85% to 87% validation accuracy in several tests. With the testing data, we observed approximately 90% accuracy in detecting and classifying the emitters.

9.7 Conclusion

In this chapter, we provided an illustration of RF signal classification using a modern machine learning approach. We discussed structure of RF signals based on various modulation schemes. We then presented various machine learning algorithms as applied to object recognition problems. We explained steps involving deep learning

Table 9.3
Deep Neural Network Configurations

Input: Batch Size × (128 × 2 × 1) Tensor
2-D Convolution, 64 count 31 × 2 kernel, followed by ReLU
2-D Convolution, 64 count 15 × 2 kernel, followed by ReLU and Batch Norm
2-D Convolution, 64 count 15 × 2 kernel, followed by ReLU
2-D Convolution, 64 count 7 × 2 kernel, followed by ReLU and Batch Norm
2-D Convolution, 64 count 15 × 2 kernel, followed by ReLU
2-D Convolution, 64 count 7 × 2 kernel, followed by ReLU and Batch Norm
Fully-Connected layer with 512 neurons, followed by ReLU and Batch Norm
Fully-Connected layer with 128 neurons, followed by ReLU and Batch Norm
Fully-Connected layer with 16 neurons, followed by Softmax

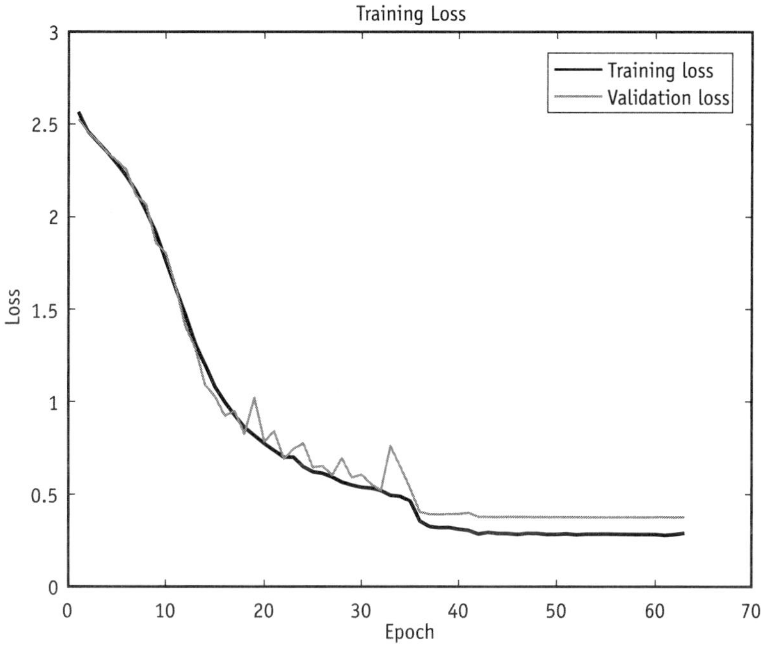

Figure 9.11
Training loss function for Wi-Fi device fingerprinting.

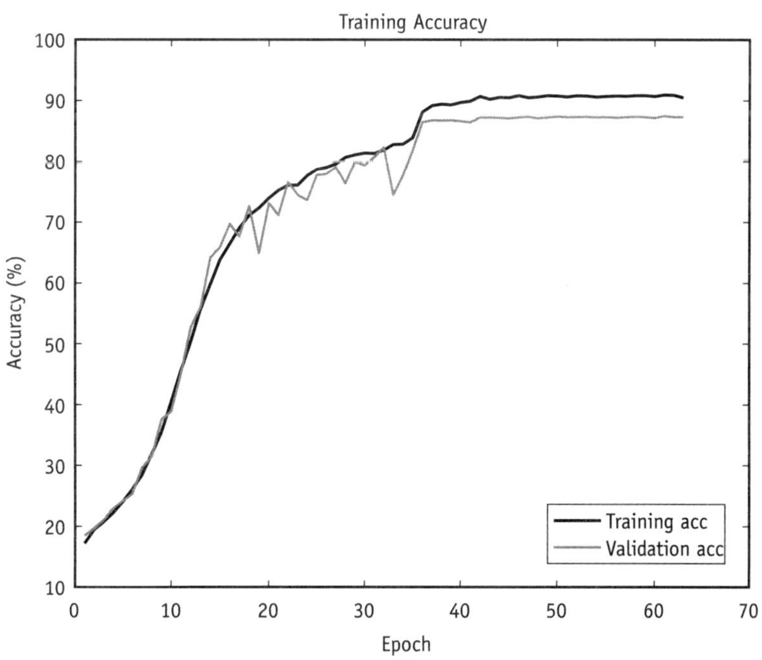

Figure 9.12
Training accuracy improvement function for Wi-Fi fingerprinting.

algorithm implementation. We provided a few RF-signal classification problems as presented in the DARPA RFMLS program. From the RFMLS problems illustrated, one can see that machine learning has much to offer for efficient use of the RF spectrum for various applications. Further, the machine learning approach can reduce the time and effort needed from human analysts. This chapter ended with a presentation of Northeastern University's ORACLE datasets for RF Wi-Fi/Emitter detection/fingerprinting. Finally, we presented a deep learning implementation of Wi-Fi signal classification.

References

[1] Krizhevsky, A., Sutskever, I., and Hinton, G. E., "Imagenet Classification with Deep Convolutional Neural Networks," *Advances in Neural Information Processing Systems*, 2012, pp. 1,097–1,105.

[2] Simonyan, K., and Zisserman, A., "Very Deep Convolutional Networks for Large-Scale Recognition," arXiv preprint, *arXiv: 1409.1556*, 2014.

[3] Szegedy, C., et al., "Going Deeper with Convolutions," *IEEE Conference on Computer Vision and Pattern Recognition*, 2015.

[4] He, K., et al., "Deep Residual Learning for Image Recognition," arXiv preprint, *arXiz:1512.03385*, 2015.

[5] *RadioFrequencyMachineLearningSystems*,https://www.darpa.mil/program/radio-frequency-machine-learning-systems.

[6] Majumder, U., Blasch, E., and Garren, D., *Deep Learning for Radar and Communications Automatic Target Recognition*, Norwood, MA: Artech House, 2020.

[7] Sankhe, K., et al. "ORACLE: Optimized Radio Classification Through Convolutional NeuraL Networks," *IEEE INFOCOM*, Paris, France, May 2019.

10

Future Trends in Signals Collection and Analysis

10.1 Introduction

The future of signals collection and analysis is likely to follow some of the recent trends in hardware technological development, sensor and communications capabilities, software infrastructure platforms, and machine data analytics. For the near term, it is reasonable to expect that the following major trends will continue:

1. Unmanned airborne vehicles, unmanned underwater vehicles, and unattended ground sensors will become smaller, cheaper, and therefore ubiquitous in many environments.
2. Signal networks will send more data via higher frequencies and high bandwidths with more finely directed power patterns to direct RF energy more efficiently to the intended receivers.
3. More devices will have some level of processing and wireless input/output capabilities, so that the Internet of Things will become one of the most significant, if not the most significant, source of RF signals in many environments.
4. Quantities of collected signals data will increase markedly due to these three issues, thereby enabling machine learning and deep learning to take increasingly more roles in the optimized

collection, detection, characterization, and exploitation of RF signals in environments of interest. ML/DL technologies can yield unanticipated applications in developing the details of future collection opportunities, and in optimizing sensor parameters to improve the amount and quality of signals data that are collected.

The following sections discuss various issues pertaining to each of these major elements of predicted capabilities in the domain of collecting, detecting, characterizing, and exploiting signals.

10.2 Unmanned Sensors

The future of signals collection and exploitation aligns well to emerging autonomous systems for such applications as autonomous cars, package delivery, and air transport.

The autonomous vehicle expectations seek to revolutionize the social way of life allowing individuals the freedom of movement. To enable such autonomy advances are needed in sensing capabilities to facilitate state awareness for scene observability, vehicle control, and coordinated action. For the automation of cars there are *levels of autonomy*:

- Level 0 (no driving automation);
- Level 1 (driver assistance);
- Level 2 (partial driving automation);
- Level 3 (conditional driving automation);
- Level 4 (high driving automation);
- Level 5 (full driving automation).

These levels of autonomy (see Figure 10.1) follow from the community analysis in aircraft levels of automation, high-level information fusion, and human-computer interaction since the inception of computers. For the pilot, the focus includes whether there is a human in, on, above, or around the loop (e.g., human in the loop (HITL)). For the computer, the focus is on whether the machine can operate in an environment that a full state of actions is available and safe. If the safety is not afforded from the environmental knowledge, the human would have to intercede.

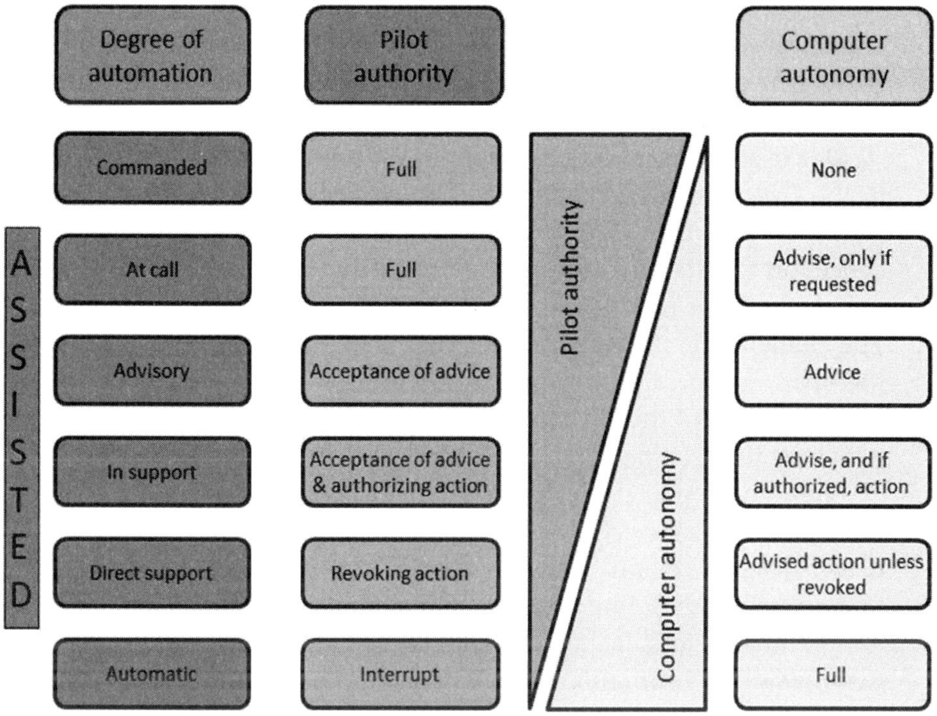

Figure 10.1
Autonomous vehicle level of autonomy. (*From:* [1].)

The future of autonomy is in sensing and signal processing. Sensing is enhanced with different types of sensors, such as 1-D temporal signals, 2-D spatial imagery, and/or multidimensional spectral analysis. Multispectral includes the frequency from which perception, communication, and coordination exist, especially for the frequency of transmission. An example is radar waveform selection for perception of synthetic aperture radar, transmission of signals, and level of control.

For perception, there are many sensor packages being developed for different autonomous platforms. Underwater vehicles typically use sonar that incorporates simultaneous location and mapping (SLAM). For unmanned aerial vehicles, electro-optical visual and infrared cameras are used for day-night vision. For autonomous cars and trucks, laser scanner, EO/IR systems, and radar are used to address scene analysis, especially with SLAM. Unattended ground sensors include seismic, acoustic, and magnetic sensors. Finally, fixed sensors from EO/IR camera systems and passive radio frequency (P-RF) support site monitoring. Together, the sensing affords analysis of situation intelligence.

One example of future capabilities with intelligence is featured in the *Experiments, Scenarios, Concept of Operations, and Prototype Engineering* (ESCAPE) data collection (see Figure 10.2). This data collection facilitates intelligence sensing through multimodal signals collections for mobile, fixed airborne, and ground sensing. The challenge is to track vehicles that move in a scene such as in the open, behind trees, or urban obscuration (e.g., going under a tunnel). Many of the approaches use multimodal data fusion from advances in machine and deep learning.

Numerous other collections exist for airborne and ground-based data collections. There are ample opportunities for researchers to design, test, and evaluate signals analytics approaches as compared to the available baseline methods that come with the collected data.

In addition to collected data, there are many simulation products for signals simulation over representative scenes such as MATLAB, AFSIM [2], and Blender. Hundreds of products exist in the

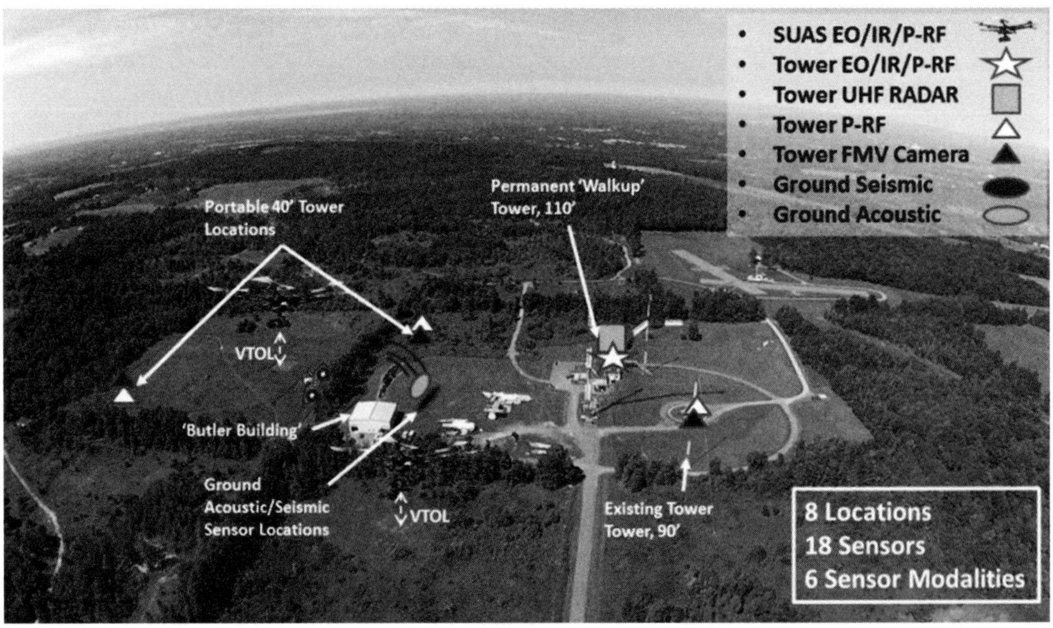

Figure 10.2

Experiments, Scenarios, Concept of Operations, and Prototype Engineering data collection. (*From:* [4].)

literature and many are available for research purposes. In addition to the collected data, the simulations provide ways to imagine future scenarios from which autonomous systems must respond. Among the many attributes of such simulators are the ability to model RF sensing and communications to enable autonomous system analysis, and especially, these approaches enable a planning tool for command and control of the sensors to determine where, when, and how to utilize sensing to improve mission performance.

10.3 Higher Frequency Communication Networks: 6G and Beyond

A significant number of signals available for collection by receiver systems in the coming decades is likely to be from mobile broadband technologies, as emanated on local cellular networks that are managed by both global and local internet service providers (ISPs). Current fifth-generation (5G) technologies enable streaming video service of movies and television shows, as well as both business and personal related video conferencing. The current 5G wireless capabilities are the latest enhancements in communications based upon radio wave, which has been the physical medium used for the previous four wireless generations of 1G, 2G, 3G, and 4G.

The next generation of mobile communications (i.e., six generation (6G)) is expected to provide virtual reality (VR) and other augmented reality technologies. These enable users to have immersive experiences interacting at other locations without traveling to them, and within other time periods, including past, possible future, and entirely fictional. Such VR capabilities will require significantly higher bandwidth communications than that of the streaming and video conferencing content of today's communications systems.

The discussion on radar in Chapter 4 clarified the essence of wireless communications, where antennas are applied at both the transmission and receiving stations within a communication system, and the type, size, and RF wavelength determine the 3-D spatial pattern of the EM power that is transferred from the transmitter to the receiver. The enhanced bandwidth requirements of 6G systems is likely to require the 30-GHz through 300-GHz radiation of millimeter waves, and might lead to the 300-GHz through 3,000-GHz waves of terahertz radiation. The power patterns at these frequencies are expected to yield mainlobe beamwidths that are as narrow as a few degrees in both angular directions, corresponding to very high transmission gains that enable the communications link budget to close between transmitter and receiver with minimal total power transferred to the antenna. The transmitting and receiver antennas are likely to be on cell towers as well as mobile broadband user equipment devices, which are most frequently in the form of smartphones and tablets. However, the use of narrow beamwidth, high gain power pattern beams on potentially moving user equipment devices will require additional real-time algorithmic processing to maintain sufficient directivity of the power pattern in the direction of the intended receiving antenna. It is likely that such processing is implemented in the form of AI/ML architectures, where volumes of past data sets are applied to train a neural network on a given piece of user equipment to optimize the communication link budget to enable the correct modulation and demodulation of symbols with a minimum of battery usage. In all, 6G-communications technologies are expected to enable high bandwidth VR-enhanced communications at higher data rates than that of current 5G systems, and on yet smaller devices that consume smaller amounts of battery power. The potential future of increasingly smaller devices operating at high frequencies and consuming less power dovetails nicely into the next discussion, the Internet of Things.

10.4 Internet of Things

The IoT refers to the increasing presence of nonhuman devices that are connected to the internet and thus generate an increasing fraction of the total RF signals in many environments. For an individual device to be a member of the IoT, it is only necessary that it have at least some type of processing capability, and it must be addressable from a local area network. In addition, it typically has the following abilities:

1. To sense some characteristics within the environment.
2. To provide actuator commands to affect some level of control within the local environment.
3. Can perform both sensor and actuator functions.

Typically, such devices communicate automatically over the internet with little or no required human involvement. The device performs certain basic functions, receives input from the surrounding environment, communicates these measurements with control systems, which then submit actuator commands to the device in order to change the process and resultant outcomes of the device.

One of the important applications is in medical treatments through devices that are embedded within human patients. For example, small devices can monitor a patient's vital signs via embedded sensors in the device; these measurements are then relayed to a monitoring system at a remote location via the internet network. These measurements can be used as training and testing in ML systems that monitor patients' health, and then relay actuator commands to dispense treatment via packet communication technologies over 6G networks and beyond. In fact, the more distant future could include the use of micromechanical devices operating within the bloodstream with communication using terahertz antennas operating at wavelengths of tens or hundreds of microns needed for communications with such small low-power devices. The future of wireless EM signals will include radio, millimeter, and terahertz waves with a multitude of devices operating with differing bandwidths, modulations, and data link layer technologies within the increasingly complicated wireless internet.

10.5 Enhanced AI/ML Applications

Though artificial intelligence/machine learning is at the forefront of signal collections and exploitation algorithms development, achieving *robust, reliable, and consistent classification* accuracy are the technical challenges that researchers must endure and deliver. Signals classification and exploitation algorithms developed under AI/ML do not provide a closed form solution. It is possible that different deep learning models may provide different results due to the datasets and models being used. Often, the developer claims high classification accuracy without mentioning enough information about the data that have been used. It is critical that training data must contain all the salient features covering as much of the operating conditions to achieve expected test data accuracy. It is possible that researchers use training data that are too small to represent operating conditions, which is commonly known as toy problem dataset. They also ignore quality of the training data such as noisy data, adversarial perturbed data, and interfered data. Thus, a comprehensive adoption of AI/ML algorithms will require a thorough understanding of the signals data used for training and developing robust AI/ML models.

10.5.1 Robust and Reliable Classifications for Noisy Signals

Deep learning has made signals and image classification models very accurate in standard operating conditions (i.e., operating on good data). Robustness to many sources of noise is a concern. A general question is if we train the network to be robust on worst-case noise: will robustness increase in general? Researchers developed algorithms called *adversarial training* that provide robust classification accuracy under adversarial or general noise perturbation. In this case, the deep neural network parameters are trained to minimize an *adversarial loss*.

In a research study [3], noisy (error) signals data have been generated by modifying phase history of 2-D synthetic aperture radar data by the following equation:

$$S_e[n,p] = S[n,p]e^{i\left(\phi_{(e,FT)}[n]+\phi_{(e,ST)}[p]\right)}$$

where, n, p are waveform samples indexed by n for all pulses p; φ is for phase error such as quadratic (αq^2), cubic (αq^3), sinusoidal ($\alpha \sin(bq)$), wideband ($\alpha N_{0,1}$); and FT and ST are fast and slow time, respectively. Figure 10.3 shows the quality of image degraded by various signal errors (intentional or unintentional).

While some of these error causes can be addressed at system design, they cannot always be mitigated by simple techniques. Additionally, algorithms such as motion compensation and autofocus intended to address these problems can be computationally burdensome.

Figure 10.4 shows that various noisy signals data have been generated (cubic, quadratic, sinusoidal, and wideband) and tested by applying various deep learning models. Among the models, ResNet18 (rn18), performed better than the others. Also, multiple polarizations exhibited superior performance accuracy. Several key results from Figure 10.4 are that severity (i.e., the level) of noise (especially, 0, 2, 4, 6, 8) reduces signal classification accuracy

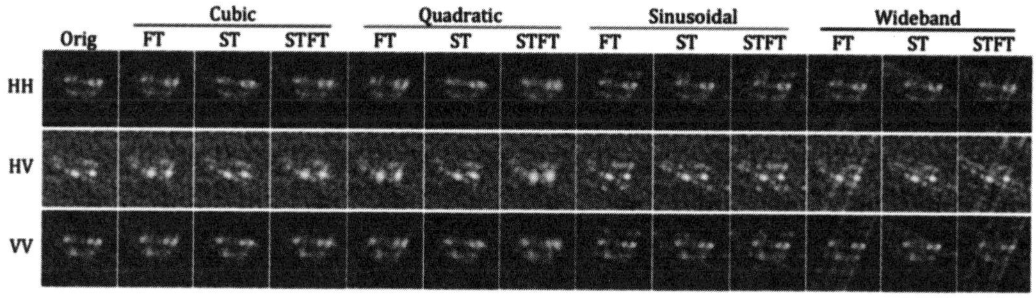

Figure 10.3
Two-dimensional signals (of synthetic aperture radar, SAR) data and image quality degradation.

model	eps	no error	cubic	quadratic	sinusoidal	wideband
aconv (HH)	0	91.91	83.79	**73.93**	44.2	33.47
	2	**92.02**	**85.62**	73.66	50.74	40.41
	4	89.98	84.19	72.47	52.24	44.76
	6	86.67	81.67	69.69	**52.33**	46.5
	8	74.97	67.71	56.02	49.32	**46.67**
convb (HH)	0	90.96	83.25	71.53	46.8	29.32
	2	**93.42**	**86.53**	73.76	52.51	36.69
	4	92.56	85.6	**73.91**	**54.2**	40.17
	6	90.26	84.01	72.89	52.2	42.15
	8	84.01	76.82	64.52	50.51	**45.06**
rn18 (HH)	0	95.67	82.11	71.83	48.56	27.61
	2	**97.84**	92.28	**79.34**	**55.08**	44.97
	4	97.56	**92.41**	78.69	54.84	53.91
	6	96.78	90.73	75.56	53.87	55.39
	8	95.51	89.42	74.39	54.55	**58.14**
aconv (MP)	0	96.06	91.06	78.98	61.52	42.03
	2	**98.46**	**94.97**	**85.08**	67.93	55.85
	4	96.35	92.37	81.64	**69.84**	61.39
	6	93.58	88.91	76.74	67.5	**63.35**
	8	83.74	79.2	68.97	61.	58.15
convb (MP)	0	94.65	91.07	78.79	65.74	40.12
	2	**98.84**	**96.3**	**86.15**	74.07	57.03
	4	97.56	94.87	85.78	**74.74**	61.74
	6	95.66	92.87	83.58	72.55	**62.12**
	8	88.98	85.15	75.26	63.89	60.05
rn18 (MP)	0	97.17	94.2	87.62	69.6	37.03
	2	**99.71**	**98.39**	**92.46**	72.26	65.47
	4	99.39	98.07	92.21	**74.01**	74.52
	6	99.24	97.83	90.5	72.05	77.
	8	98.71	97.02	89.01	71.23	**78.73**

Figure 10.4
Two-dimensional signals (images of vehicles) classification accuracy with various levels and types of noises. It is noted that wideband noise signals cause huge problems and causes significant accuracy degradation.

regardless of the deep learning models that are used. Amongst various deep leaning models, ResNet18 is a robust model to be used for noisy signals classification. It was interesting to see that multiple polarizations signals perform better in noisy environments. Finally, among the types of noises, wideband noises have detrimental impact on signals classification.

10.5.2 Signals Classification Algorithm's Performance Evaluations

As mentioned earlier, AI/ML-based signals classification algorithms do not provide a closed form solution. Hence, we must develop a thorough test and evaluation (T&E) plan to trust and verify signals classification accuracy provided by the AI/ML algorithms. The Tables 10.1 and 10.2 show the goals of various data models and test and evaluation.

In summary, to develop future signals collection and processing systems based on AI/ML, we must address the adversarial noise impact on classification accuracy reduction. For this reason, we must develop datasets covering various operating conditions. Finally, we must develop a through test and evaluation plan to trust and verify deep learning models.

Table 10.1
Data Models Needed for Robust AI/ML Algorithm Development

Mathematical performance analysis	Analytical model
Robust parameter exploration	Simulation model
Real data collected from sensors	Empirical model
Observations of humans with systems	Process model

Table 10.2
Goals of Various T&E for AI/ML Algorithm Evaluation

Innovative test and evaluation (IT&E)	Exploratory
Design test and evaluation (DT&E)	Development
Operational test and evaluation (OT&E)	Utilization
Software test and evaluation (ST&E)	Capability

10.6 Conclusion

It is possible to make reasonable short-term predictions about the wireless signals that comprise the spectrum of the near futures. First, the use of unmanned sensors is becoming more prevalent in recent years, and this trend is expected to continue. These technologies enable sensing and actuator capabilities at remote locations with a very low barrier to entry, due to the decreasing costs of such sensors. Second, the wireless signals of 6G and beyond are expected to involve the higher 30 GHz to 300 GHz of millimeter waves and possibly 300 GHz to 3,000 GHz of waves in the more distant future. These higher frequencies are likely to use narrow beamwidth, high gain power patterns to close the power link budget with minimal power requirements. Third, this migration to higher frequencies is expected in the future of a higher percentage of IoT devices within the wireless internet traffic. Finally, AI and ML are expected to be important technologies that will play ever more important roles in processing large amounts of data, and thus in the collection of wireless signals in the near and more distant future.

References

[1] Degrees of autonomy, https://commons.wikimedia.org/wiki/File:Degrees_of_autonomy.jpg.

[2] "AFSIM: The Air Force Research Laboratory's Approach to Making M&S Ubiquitous in the Weapon System Concept Development Process," https://csiac.org/articles/afsim-the-air-force-research-laboratorys-approach-to-making-ms-ubiquitous-in-the-weapon-system-concept-development-process/.

[3] Inkawhich, N., et al., "Advanced Techniques for Robust SAR ATR: Mitigating Noise and Phase Errors," *2020 IEEE International Radar Conference (RADAR)*, 2020, pp. 844–849,DOI: 10.1109/RADAR42522.2020.9114784.

[4] Zulch, P., Distasio, M., Cushman T., Wilson B., Hart B., and Blasch E., "ESCAPE Data Collection for Multi-Modal Data Fusion Research," *2019 IEEE Aerospace Conference*, Big Sky, MT, March 2–9, 2019.

About the Authors

David A. Garren has held the rank of professor in the Electrical and Computer Engineering Department, Naval Postgraduate School (NPS), in Monterey, California, since 2020, after entering with the rank of associate professor in 2012. Prior to his academic career, he had over 25 years of industry experience in applied research in various disciplines, including radar, image processing, and signal processing. He has 23 refereed journal publications and over 50 conference publications. He is the author of seven U.S. patents, all pertaining to radar, and is a senior member of the Institute of Electrical and Electronics Engineers (IEEE). In 2020, he coauthored the textbook *Deep Learning for Radar and Communications Automatic Target Recognition*. In addition, he currently is serving as senior editor in the electronic warfare section of the *IEEE Transactions on Aerospace and Electronic Systems*, after having served as an associate editor for the journal from 2019 to 2020. Also, while at NPS, he served as principal investigator for numerous research projects sponsored by various federal government agencies.

Professor Garren received a BS as salutatorian from Roanoke College in 1986 with a double major in mathematics and physics, and a concentration in computer science. He received an MS and PhD in physics from William & Mary in 1988 and 1991, respectively. He was awarded a competitive Office of Naval Research (ONR) Postdoctoral Fellowship at the Naval Research Laboratory (NRL) from 1991 through 1993. From 1994 through 2012, he held positions at two Fortune 500 defense companies while performing research in several technologies, including radar, signal processing, and modeling. His industry service culminated with being awarded the titles of both Technical Fellow and Assistant Vice President at one of these companies. Professor Garren enjoys sharing his experience in applied research and teaching to NPS graduate students as part of their service to the defense of the U.S. and allied nations.

Uttam K. Majumder is a senior staff scientist and portfolio lead for radar AI/ML at the U.S. Department of Defense. His research interests include artificial intelligence/machine learning (AI/ML) for automatic target recognition (ATR), high-performance computing (HPC), synthetic aperture radar (SAR), algorithms development for surveillance applications, radar waveforms design, and digital image processing. Among various awards, Dr. Majumder received the U.S. Air Force's Civilian Achievement Award for distinguished performance, AFRL's Science and Technology Achievement Award for radar systems development, and SPIE Rising Researcher Award for machine learning algorithms development.

Dr. Majumder earned his BS from the Department of Computer Science, The City College of New York (CCNY), an MS from the Air Force Institute of Technology, Dayton, Ohio, and a PhD in Electrical Engineering from Purdue University, West Lafayette, Indiana. He also received an MBA from Wright State University, Dayton, Ohio. Dr. Majumder served as an adjunct faculty at Wright State University where he developed and taught a graduate course on SAR signal and image processing. Dr. Majumder has published more than 50 technical papers (for journals and conferences) with IEEE, SPIE, MILCOM, and Tri-Service Radar Symposium. He submitted two patent applications. Dr. Majumder is a senior member of IEEE and SPIE. He is a reviewer of IEEE TAES and serves as a technical program committee and session chair for multiple conferences. Dr. Majumder is a distinguish lecturer and short-course instructor for IEEE AESS on the topic Deep Learning for Radar ATR.

Erik P. Blasch is a program officer at the U.S. Air Force Research Laboratory (AFRL)–Air Force Office of Scientific Research (AFOSR) in Arlington, Virginia. Previously, he was a principal scientist at the AFRL Information Directorate in Rome, New York (2012 to 2017), an exchange scientist to the Defense Research and Development

Canada (DRDC) in Valcartier, Quebec (2010 to 2012), and information fusion evaluation tech lead for the AFRL Sensors Directorate–Comprehensive Performance Assessment of Sensor Exploitation (COMPASE) center in Dayton, Ohio (2000 to 2009). Additional assignments include USAF Reserve Officer Colonel supporting intelligence, acquisition, and space technology with 18 medals. Academically, he was an adjunct associate professor in electrical and biomedical engineering (2000 to 2010) at Wright State University and the Air Force Institute of Technology (AFIT) teaching classes in signal processing, electronics, and information fusion as well as research adjunct appointments (2011 to 2017) at the University of Dayton, Binghamton University, and Rochester Institute of Technology.

Dr. Blasch was a founding member of the International Society of Information Fusion (ISIF), (www.isif.org), 2007 president, and Board of Governors (2000 to 2010). He served on the IEEE Aerospace and Electronics Systems Society (AESS) Board of Governors (2011 to 2016), distinguished lecturer (2012 to 2019), cochair of five conferences, and associate editor of three academic journals. He has focused on information fusion, target tracking, robotics, and pattern recognition research compiling over 850 scientific papers and book chapters. He holds 43 patents, received 33 team-robotics awards, presented over 60 tutorials, and provided 12 plenary talks. His coauthored books include *High-Level Information Fusion Management and Systems Design* (Artech House, 2012), *Context-Enhanced Information Fusion* (Springer, 2016), *Multispectral Image Fusion and Colorization* (SPIE, 2018), and *Handbook of Dynamic Data Driven Applications Systems* (Springer, 2018).

Dr. Blasch received his BS in mechanical engineering from the Massachusetts Institute of Technology (1992) and MS in mechanical engineering (1994), health science (1995), and industrial engineering (human factors) (1995) from Georgia Tech, and attended the University of Wisconsin for a MD/PhD in neuroscience/mechanical engineering until being called to military service in 1996 to the U.S. Air Force. He completed an MBA (1998), MS in economics (1999), and PhD in electrical engineering (1999) from Wright State University, and is a graduate of Air War College (2008). He is the recipient of the IEEE Bioengineering Award (Russ–2008), IEEE AESS magazine best paper award (Mimno–2012), Military Sensing

Symposium leadership in Data Fusion Award (Mignogna–2014), Fulbright scholar selection (2017), and 18 research/technical and team awards from AFRL. He is an American Institute of Aeronautics and Astronautics (AIAA) Associate Fellow, Society of Photonics and Industrial Engineers (SPIE) Fellow, and IEEE Fellow.

Index

Artech House
Intelligence and Information Operations Library

Ed Waltz, Series Editor

Activity-Based Intelligence: Principles and Applications, Patrick Biltgen and Stephen Ryan

Advances in Statistical Multisource-Multitarget Information Fusion, Ronald P. S. Mahler

The Art and Science of Military Deception, Hy Rothstein and Barton Whaley

Aviation Security Engineering: A Holistic Approach, Rainer Kölle, Garik Markarian, and Alex Tarter

Concepts, Models, and Tools for Information Fusion, Éloi Bossé, Jean Roy, and Steve Wark

Counterdeception Principles and Applications for National Security, Michael Bennett

Cyberwarfare: An Introduction to Information-Age Conflict, Isaac R. Porche III

Data Fusion Support to Activity-Based Intelligence, Richard T. Antony

Designing Wireless Sensor Network Solutions for Tactical ISR, Timothy D. Cole

Essential Principles of Signals Collection and Analysis, David A. Garren, Uttam K. Majumder, and Erik P. Blasch

Geospatial Data, Information, and Intelligence, Aaron Jabbour and Renny Babiarz

High-Level Data Fusion, Subrata Das

High-Level Information Fusion Management and Systems Design, Erik Blasch, Éloi Bossé, and Dale A. Lambert, editors

Homeland Security Technology Challenges: From Sensing and Encrypting to Mining and Modeling, Giorgio Franceschetti and Marina Grossi, editors

Human-Centered Information Fusion, David L. Hall and John M. Jordan

Information Fusion and Analytics for Big Data and IoT, Éloi Bossé and Basel Solaiman

Information Warfare and Organizational Decision-Making, Alexander Kott, editor

Information Operations Planning, Patrick D. Allen

Information Warfare and Electronic Warfare Systems,
Richard A. Poisel

Information Warfare Principles and Operations, Edward Waltz

Knowledge Management in the Intelligence Enterprise,
Edward Waltz

Mathematical Techniques in Multisensor Data Fusion, Second Edition, David L. Hall and Sonya A. H. McMullen

Naval ISR Fusion Principles, Operations, and Technologies,
Jim Scrofani, Will Williamson, Jihane Mimih, and Ed Waltz

Principles of Data Fusion Automation, Richard T. Antony

Sensor Management in ISR, Kenneth J. Hintz

Strategem: Deception and Surprise in War, Barton Whaley

Statistical Multisource-Multitarget Information Fusion,
Ronald P. S. Mahler

For further information on these and other Artech House titles, including previously considered out-of-print books now available through our In-Print-Forever® (IPF®) program, contact:

Artech House
685 Canton Street
Norwood, MA 02062
Phone: 781-769-9750
Fax: 781-769-6334
e-mail: artech@artechhouse.com

Artech House
16 Sussex Street
London SW1V 14RW UK
Phone: +44 (0)20-7596-8750
Fax: +44 (0)20-7630-0166
e-mail: artech-uk@artechhouse.com

Find us on the World Wide Web at: www.artechhouse.com